CW00381188

new
colour
healing

new colour healing

A PRACTICAL GUIDE TO UNDERSTANDING THE HEALING POWER OF COLOUR

LILIAN VERNER-BONDS

Vermilion
LONDON

2 3 4 5 6 7 8 9 10

Copyright © Lilian Verner-Bonds 2002

Lilian Verner-Bonds has asserted her moral right
to be identified as the author of this work in accordance
with the Copyright, Design and Patents Act 1988.

All rights reserved. No part of this publication may be reproduced,
stored in a retrieval system, or transmitted in any form by means,
electronic, mechanical, photocopying, recording or otherwise,
without the prior permission of the copyright owner.

First published in the United Kingdom in 2002 by Vermilion,
an imprint of Ebury Press
Random House UK Ltd.
Random House
20 Vauxhall Bridge Road
London SW1V 2SA

Random House Australia (Pty) Limited
20 Alfred Street, Milsons Point, Sydney,
New South Wales 2061, Australia

Random House New Zealand Limited
18 Poland Road, Glenfield,
Auckland 10, New Zealand

Random House (Pty) Limited
Endulini, 5A Jubilee Road, Parktown 2193, South Africa

Random House UK Limited Reg. No. 954009
www.randomhouse.co.uk
Papers used by Vermilion are natural, recyclable products
made from wood grown in sustainable forests.

A CIP catalogue record is available
for this book from the British Library.

ISBN: 0091883865

Designed and typeset by seagulls
Printed and bound in Great Britain by Mackays of Chatham plc, Chatham, Kent

**Nothing in this book is to be construed as taking the place
of appropriate medical advice, diagnosis or treatment.**

While the case histories described in this book are based on real people and their
experiences, the author created pseudonyms and altered identifying characteristics to
preserve the privacy and anonymity of the individuals and their families. The author
is grateful to the clients who allowed their stories to be shared.

DEDICATION

To my daughter Louise Jane Verner/Marsh,
the joy and light of my life,
and
to my son-in-law Lawrence Marsh,
a very special man.

**With thanks and appreciation to my editor,
Dr Ronald L. Bonewitz, PhD**

AUTHOR PROFILE

Lilian Verner-Bonds is one of the world's leading colour therapists, clairvoyant palmists and healers, and an international
lecturer, teacher and author. She has written numerous books on
colour, colour-zone therapy and palmistry. Her tape *The Healing
Rainbow*, along with a musical *Colour Healing* CD, is regarded
as a classic. Her work is widely recognised throughout Australia,
Europe and America, where she appears regularly on radio and
television giving psychic phone-ins, and on other programmes
related to the mystic arts. She is Vice President and past
Chairman of the International Association of Colour Therapists.

contents

introduction

I have always known about my psychic gifts. Even as a successful actress, the gift was there. Later I learned to harness the power and channel it into colour therapy. Colour is an integral part of the make-up of human beings; it is a psychic sense.

Colour therapy is individual. The art of the colour therapist is first to assess by the use of colour, to use colour in an intuitive way, and then to find the unique treatment for the person.

Colour sets you free. If you do not know why something keeps happening in your life, why you are having the same illness, why you feel the same negative reactions to someone or something, why you are stuck in useless patterns of behaviour, then colour therapy will help. Colour can reveal the significance of our actions that cannot otherwise be observed.

Colour therapy is enabling. It allows individuals to discover new things about themselves, about others, and about the world in general. It will enable you to use colour in your everyday life; simple techniques can help you to make your own assessment – mentally, emotionally, physically, and spiritually. Discover the magic of colour ...

Lilian Verner-Bonds
London, 2002

1

the sense
of colour

Rainbow Puddles

'When did you first discover that colour was magic?' someone once asked me. I thought about this. Then I remembered the rainbow puddles.

As a child I was absolutely amazed when it rained and oil that had been spilled from the cars on the road became the most exquisite patches of rainbow puddles. I would spend hours sitting on the kerb, my chin cupped in my hands, staring into these patches that seemed to come alive when the rain poured on them. It was a real joy. I loved it when it rained because I knew that the rainbow puddles would appear again. I found them so ... It was like a deep... It took my breath away ...

I can even feel it now. I used to feel such a fullness – a contentment came into my stomach as I sat there looking at the colours. It was beautiful. A great sense of well-being used to come over me. I was happy. I used to point them out to people, but nobody took any notice. I used to say, 'Look at all the colours,' and they used to say, 'Yes,' and move on. They had no interest in them. When the puddle dried the colours disappeared and I knew I would have to wait until it rained again. It wasn't as if there was a patch of grease on the road where I thought there was going to be a rainbow. I didn't see anything until it rained, and then they popped up all over the place, like magic.

As a dyslexic, I had at last found my key to communication. I could read at last: I could read the language of colour.

Colour's 'Open Sesame'

Colour is a vibration, it shimmers. Each colour of the spectrum vibrates at a slightly different rate from the one either side of it, and we appreciate the beauty of each. But there is more than beauty in a colour for me. I would like to explain to you what my personal experience of colour is wherever I encounter it, and how I put that into practice when I work with my clients, or with the public, or in fact in any area where my knowledge of colour needs to be harnessed for health, healing and enlightenment.

If I'm in a room that is blue, and I feel a certain kind of sensation in my body, I know that there is some information for me in that colour. It is as though the blue is trying to contact me. It is not always the same feeling. It can be physical or it can be emotional. Sometimes it will be a slight tightening or slight fluttering in my solar plexus, as of fear; another time it will be a feeling of opening, of lightening. But whatever form it takes, it always involves one or more of my senses.

When I feel this signal I simply give myself over to the colour. I know that if I allow myself to be immersed in the blue I will understand what it is I need – or what it is I don't need. If I am willing to listen, the colour will tell me.

We all have colours radiating out of us all the time. Every organ has a colour. The colours often come out in little puffs, although sometimes I can look intently at a person and their physical body dissolves and leaves just an outline where they were, into which I can see. Then I witness a multitude of colour rays coming out from all parts of their body. Their outer flesh goes, and I can see the patches of different colours that are their organs. There is, in fact, a level at which the person is a colour body, like Joseph's coat of many colours.

This inner colour body gives us information about ourselves and others. If an organ is not functioning properly it will not send out a strong, brightly coloured light. The colour will be dim and weak. Sometimes the organ will appear to be dark, indicating that it is not as healthy as it could be.

I was at a seminar. The room was full of people but my eyes were drawn to a young man sitting some distance away. He seemed very animated and very happy ... but I could see little puffs of colour, little lilac puffballs, coming from his body. I quite often see this with people, little puffs of colour that are shaped like a ball. They always come from around the head and pop out upwards. In this young man's case, they were a pale lilac. I knew I had to say something, so I went over and sat next to him.

We started talking and after a minute or two I told him that I thought it would be a good idea for him to look to his immune system at this time because it needed some strengthening. Tears came into his eyes and he told me that he had been diagnosed as HIV positive a week before the seminar.

The young man at the seminar didn't have to tell me that he didn't feel well. In his case it was the colour coming from his body that told me what was wrong. But there are other ways. In a private reading, for instance, I would have asked him to select some colours from my colour table.

When I ask people to choose colours they are drawn to the colours which connect with their own inner colour vibrations. The colours they choose intuitively, and the sequence in which they choose them, give me information about their physical, emotional and mental states. This can be information about their present state, but it can also be about their birth, first months, childhood, adolescence, any time – even pre-birth, and pre-conception. This is another aspect of colour's magic: it opens up a door into a person's history, like Aladdin's 'open sesame' at the cave entrance – and not only into the past, as the colour body sometimes seems to know the future as well.

A woman came to see me. She chose some colours and I told her that she had just chosen the colour of birthing. I saw two children before 18 months were up, although for some reason I found myself telling her that she would only have one. She was not particularly pleased by this information and said that she couldn't see how she was going to have even one because she had no intention of having any. I was a bit puzzled myself. How could she have two children in 18 months?

Four years later I met her at a cocktail party. She came over to me, smiling, and pointed to the three-year-old boy holding her hand. 'You were right,' she said, 'I did get pregnant. I had twins but I lost one, and here is my son.' The little boy looked at me and I felt I knew him well. He had, after all, let us know he was coming!

Her conscious self had been convinced of one thing but her colour body had known better. Something within her on a subtle level was already working, propelling her on a course that she was as yet not aware of.

Following Colour Into the Body – And Beyond

Colour goes beyond the surface. We can see with our eyes, but colour sees deeper, and further.

Colour sees right through us. It doesn't stop at the surface of the body, nor at the surface of time and space either. At every moment colour is streaming effortlessly through our bodies like light through a window. Colour can reveal the significance of our actions that could not otherwise be observed.

When I am seeing with colour I see as though I have become the colour that shows up for that person. Then I can see through into the body: I see with the eyes of colour. Another way of putting it is that the energy of colour is like an X-ray that allows me to penetrate through the skin-deep physical body to the organs and parts within.

It is not just the body now, as it is in the present moment, that I see. Colour seems to open up a person's body to me from the time it was conceived. The body on the chair in front of me is open; but so also is that body which stretches away from this present moment back to its conception. I call this the 'time body'.

Someone chooses a dark green. I become that dark green myself, and then I can go into their situation on the wave or vibration of the colour. In the physical body, the dark green may lead back to inflammation of the joints – rheumatism for instance. 'Rheuma' is the Greek for 'flow' – the flow of subtle energy through the body. The energy travels in waves through our tissue fluids. Dark green represents resentment. In relation to rheumatism it indicates a child who was manoeuvred in a direction that was not in harmony with his or her abilities and talents. The child was misdirected, its aspiration smothered by a wet flannel. The resulting pattern of behaviour can be summed up in one word: reluctance – and so can rheumatism.

Rheumatism with its stiffness, its inflammation and swelling, is a physical form of the emotional response of resistance. The child could not resist successfully, but what it did do was stiffen like a dog being pulled on a lead against its will. When muscles stiffen the flow of rheuma is impeded, even cut off. If this pattern of muscular resistance continues all our life, our body chemistry changes, and if we continue to live with this chemical make-up, rheumatism/arthritis eventually become the physical symptoms. The pushing around does not necessarily cease just because we grow larger and become adults. When the rheuma flow is held up for long enough the machinery of the body suffers, particularly the muscles, ligaments and joints. The outcome is the familiar symptom picture of rheumatism – the degeneration of muscles and joints, and the resulting inflammation and swellings.

It is important to understand that when we are being pushed around as children we react *emotionally* as well as physically. Not to be treated as whom and what we really are by our parents is emotionally painful. To be treated as a future accountant when you are really a future dancer is traumatic in its denial and suppression of your real vocation. The emotional pain can be so great, in fact, that we can only deal with it by going numb. I have often experienced this emotional numbness with rheumatic sufferers. It is as though the unfelt and long-stored emotional pain has come out as physical pain and degeneration. Thus, rheumatism has a strong emotional component. This is the resentment of dark green. In the person's time body it may be something that happened when they were five, or the same thing happening many times. The green will take me to the area of their body that is being affected by the resentment, and also back in time to the origin of their pattern of resentment.

The same colour does not always lead to the same place. Another person may choose dark green and we will end up somewhere quite different in their body or their life. Heart conditions, jealousy, envy and greed are all negative aspects of green.

It's only after a person has chosen a particular colour that I am able to 'tune-in' to its vibration and discover information relating specifically to the client.

A colour can pinpoint an event, but it can also point to a general predisposition within the person. One of the negative aspects of indigo, for instance, is connected with addiction and obsession. So someone choosing indigo could signal a tendency towards physical addiction. It could also express itself as extreme devotion. Perhaps the person has become emotionally obsessed with someone or some cause, or obsessed by certain ideas which they cannot let go. In the realm of past lives, indigo might lead back to a lifetime of devotion and austerity as a monk in a monastery, or maybe show a lack of structure in previous lives. The particular events for two people who choose indigo are likely to be quite different, but they will usually relate to the general themes of the colour.

Colour also speeds up the therapy process. Working with colour saves a great deal of talking – something which is sometimes the cause of suspicion in our word-centred society. Using colours that a client has intuitively chosen means that I don't have to ask what their mother did, what their father did and what everybody else did. It shortens therapy time immensely because, on the first reading, I know exactly where we are going. We don't have to spend a long time finding out what the person's issues are.

There is often some confusion about 'therapy'. The general idea is that you only need therapy if you are psychologically ill in some way, if you have some psychological condition that more or less incapacitates you the way flu or cancer does physically. For some this is true enough, and many people do come to me with specific complaints, physical and psychological. However, when we go to a therapist we are also asking for support or assistance. We may not be aware that this puts us in a state of humility – which allows us to be teachable. When we are teachable we are ready to learn and grow. Ralph Waldo Emerson said, 'What lies behind us and what lies before us does not compare with what lies within us.'

Many people come, both for private consultations and to my public seminars, who do not need 'therapy' in the normal sense. Their aim is wider: they are seeking enlightenment – to 'know themselves'. My function as a therapist is to be a catalyst (a catalyst being an agent that effects change without becoming involved itself), that is to be available for people while they enlighten themselves.

The Journey to Our True Self

Colour, my clients' and my own experiences have taught me, can be as magical as any stage in our journey along the path to our true self. So many clues to our current difficulties and dilemmas lie in our earliest days, and sometimes even earlier.

We are all born in truth. As babies, every single one of us knows only the real self which is creative and divine. The truth is the real self. The untrue self, like negativity, will have to be learned. All children react spontaneously to the truth. But if someone says to them, 'Don't do that,' the child will think, 'Oh dear, I'd better obey. If I don't I might not be liked,' and the subconscious belief would be: if I'm not liked, I could be abandoned, and then I would die. Because of this threat to basic survival he will respond by ignoring his spontaneous truthfulness and work from the adapted self – the fake self – because he is rewarded for this. According to how far a child has to go along with this will affect how they function. Eventually they may operate only from the adapted self. The child's identity becomes 'I adapt', but later the child may have an identity crisis, 'Who am I?' This does not mean adults must not give guidance to a child. All children need appropriate direction that their parents' experience can give them. What they don't need is indoctrination.

Truth allows us to be authentic, which enables us to be authors of our own experience. It gives us the authority to direct our own lives. Truthfulness is spontaneous. It happens on the moment and is never the same twice. That's why it can be so frightening. You can't measure the truth, and modern man is so keen to measure everything, to feel secure, that an imbalance occurs which actually interrupts the flow of truth. A very simple way to break this pattern is to take a long deep breath, filling the lungs to capacity. A breath taken like this short-circuits the rational mind and frees us to flow again. The false self knows and remembers by habit, by addiction. The real self is not addicted. It always does things for the first time. The false self always tries to hang on to form or matter because of its compulsion to seek security no matter what, which brings about a descent of spirit. Its idea of emotion is negative emotion, which includes all the fears, greed, envy and jealousies. Every negative emotion is learned. It is not natural to us. It comes from the fear of survival, the fear that the universe won't look after us. Because of this lack of trust we have to learn to manipulate our environment in order to be safe.

Emotions are the only reliable truth. An emotion is a chemical event that is experienced in the body. The emotion is always the first reaction we have to something. After the emotion comes the feeling, so when I say I feel this or that an emotion has already happened in my body and right now I can express the feeling I have from it. After this I will interpret the feeling that followed the emotion and then I will act on the interpretation, or not. How we interpret the feeling will relate to how we experienced our environment as a child. When we are afraid of emotion we are afraid of the truth.

Emotions do not have to run away with you. They enhance your communications and relationships. They provide another dimension and help you to have a richer existence. So the false self is adapted behaviour. It's the behaviour I learned would be *all right*. It learns an habitual response; it's not creative, it becomes ritualistic, compulsive, obsessive.

All addictions are another way of obliterating the pain of not being allowed to be who we are. Adaptations in early childhood are responsible for much suffering and unhappiness in adulthood. We never fully lose our inner knowing of truth, but we may have become so conditioned that we find these negative patterns of behaviour extremely difficult to break, so difficult that we may be pushed to the extreme act of ending it all. To get back to who we really are can have extreme consequences. I believe that when a person commits suicide it is a last vain attempt to get back or forward to a moment of truth. It may be the only way a person can connect with the identity of the true self. After all, the moment of death is a fundamental truth – unfortunately it will interrupt the span of natural life.

Since being is related to feeling, it is also related to those spontaneous and involuntary movements and gestures that constitute true self-expression. In our spontaneous movements and utterances, we experience directly the life force within us. We will always subconsciously strive to get back to a state of truth. Truth will always dissolve the fake self. It is the real, divine self incarnated in the body as 'me'. It is a state of grace.

The Colours of Self-Knowing

Colour is a whole new dimension of self-discovery. With colour you can totally disassemble yourself, then reassemble yourself with something new. Getting to know yourself is an essential part of life, some would say the most essential. Looking at it from a purely practical level, we are likely to function better when we know what we are and how we work – or don't work.

People have always known this truth. The great philosopher Socrates devoted much of his life to reminding his fellow citizens of this in Athens, over 2,000 years ago. We may be more advanced technologically than the ancient Greeks, but we have not escaped from the necessity to 'know thyself'.

To further this process of self-knowing by any one of the many forms of counselling that depend upon talking, upon words, is of some help. The trouble is that we will usually answer the questions from the conscious mind only. My experience is that we need to go further, deeper than that. We have to go into our subconscious to be able to get to the real truth. Only then does the work of knowing ourselves begin to bring about permanent changes, enabling us to free our present actions and relationships from the old hurts and fears of childhood.

We are all made up of light and darkness. One way into the hidden side of ourselves is to explore darkness and silence, and also the black (see Chapter 7).

Black has a special magic in this journey to our shadow self. Black is known as the non-colour. With black there is no crutch – it is the colour that makes you stand on your own. If we dare to embrace black, it becomes the liberator. When we are able to embrace and love that 'delinquent' part of our child-selves as much as the 'good' part, we are free from its grip and in a state of grace. But it isn't easy. These old memories and connections are hidden from us for a good reason. There is often much pain clinging to them. In a very real way, the child we once were still exists within us, and is still suffering.

An old Chinese sage is reported to have said to his students: 'I can turn back one corner for you. The rest you will have to do for yourselves.' Like Socrates, he, too, was speaking of the work that in our time has come to be called 'personal growth': the work of coming to know who you are, how you got to be that way, and what you can do about it. Dogged persistence is sometimes required to remain on our path of self-discovery. But colour can help enormously.

And if, as weeks go round, in the dark of the moon
my spirit darkens and goes out, and soft strange gloom
pervades my movements and my thoughts and words
then I shall know I am walking still
with God, we are closer together now the moon's
in shadow.

Shadows, D.H. Lawrence

The Intelligence of Colour – The Pure Light

Sometimes when giving a colour-reading, a client says to me: 'How do you know this?' I used to wonder myself: How on earth do I know this? I wanted some complicated explanation. Since I have accepted the magic of colour, I've been able to accept the simplicity of the answer: I know because the colours tell me.

Each colour can have many meanings. The crunch in being a colour therapist comes in knowing how the colour relates personally to the client. For me it is a matter of listening. I don't know what the story is going to be this time. The colour tells me. What I have to do is empty myself of myself so that I can first hear, and then translate, its message. As the quote from D.H. Lawrence's poem puts it: 'Not I, not I, but the wind which blows through me!' For me, the wind is coloured.

Colour is a language. I simply know what the script means. I listen to what the colour is saying and try to translate it into English. It can be difficult; sometimes I have to struggle to find the words I need to convey exactly what it is saying. And sometimes there are no words.

Someone asked me what, or who, is speaking to me in this colour language. I have thought about this often and will try to give an answer. Colour comes out of pure light. The clear light that holds all colour is the clear brilliance. It is the cosmic law or, if you prefer, the 'universal intelligence'. Light is an intelligence, a higher order of intelligence, so colour can be seen as the way light talks to us. When the light from the Sun and the stars reaches the Earth the colours of the spectrum break out of its brilliance. It's like birth. I wonder sometimes whether it must be painful for a colour to be born out of the light.

Physical science tells us that all light is visible, radiant energy that travels through space in wave form at a speed of 186,000 miles per second. The light vibrates at different wavelengths and frequencies. Red has the longest wavelength and violet the shortest. The speed at which it travels has a great effect upon anything that receives it.

We react to colour automatically. It influences our thoughts, our social behaviour, our health, our relationships; in fact we cannot live without the light which contains all colour. If you put a plant in a cupboard and shut out the light it withers and dies.

Colour can be measured. All organs and parts of our bodies, when they are healthy, hold to a particular set of harmonious vibrations. It has been proved that it is part and parcel of the psychic, emotional and physical make-up of human beings. We are given this proof that light is not only without, shining on us, but that it is also a part of us, within, in our dreams. When you go to sleep at night, you have your eyes shut in a dark room and yet you see your dreams. Have you ever considered where the light comes from to illuminate your dreams? It must surely come from within. The light was and is always with you – your dreams are proof of this. If we dream in black and white it is of the past while a colourful dream is of the future. A nightmare represents a 'backslip'. Even if the nightmare is in colour, its origins come from the past.

A simple source of light is a candle. A candle represents the light in the darkness. It also represents the uncertainty of life, as it is easily extinguishable. As dreams show the light within, candles represent the light without – our essential self. People who have had near-death experiences often remark on the light that leads the way. No wonder light has been considered divine – the divine light (from where all colour comes from) that leads the world.

We cannot close ourselves off to this intelligence. Light quietly sustains us through every moment. We can blinker ourselves and forget this crucial, life-giving relationship.

Our knowledge of colour has never ever been truly lost. How could it ever be? As long as the sun continues to shine upon the Earth and its colours speak to us it can be ignored but not lost. In every age, those willing to learn its language will be given the gift of the healing wisdom it contains, and directly experience the deep benevolence that the intelligence which speaks through colour has towards us in our struggle with life.

The Ages of Colour

The present era is called 'the *colour age*'. People are beginning to give recognition to colour's vital influence. History has shown that colour has always thrilled and fascinated human beings since the beginning of time. Even though we have modern technology, the world is turning with renewed interest to the study of light, reviewing and understanding ancient healing methods as well as examining modern scientific data.

Colour leads us into virtually all realms of human life and culture. Colour healing is not a new idea, something that the 'New Age' has discovered. In 1937, M. Luckeish in his book, *The Science of Seeing,* wrote: 'One should not be surprised if it is revealed some time in the future when we know more about the human being, that all wavelengths of radiant energy from the sun are intricately entwined in the life and health processes of human beings.'

Kate W. Baldwin, MD, FAGS, former Senior Surgeon, Women's Hospital, Philadelphia, also observed 'I can produce quicker and more accurate results with colour than with any, or all, other methods combined; and with less strain on the patient.'

There were schools of colour healing in Ancient Egypt. In his book, *The Seven Keys to Colour Healing,* the famous colour researcher Roland Hunt, writes: 'In the ancient temples of Heliopolis, Egypt, the force of colour was used, not only as an aid to worship, but also as a healing agent. These temples were oriented so that the sun shone through in such a way that its light was broken up into seven prismatic colours and suffering ones were bathed in that special colour which they needed to restore them to health.' In China many centuries ago, people found that when they wrapped their bodies in red silk and placed themselves out in the sun it prevented scarring from smallpox.

Our civilisation's temples of healing are churches. In these, the memory of the ancient knowledge of the healing power of colour can be seen in the stained-glass windows. When the sun shines through the coloured windows and floods the congrega- tion in healing light, they are being bathed in colour in just the same way as in Ancient Egypt. Throughout history healing always came from inspiration and intuitiveness, coupled with as much scientific knowledge as was available at the time. In the eighteenth century society changed its view and understanding of enlightenment – there was a sudden swing to intellectual consciousness and rationality. A new era, the Age of Reason, had begun. The local tea rooms were full of ideas and ways of thinking; poets wrote about the new trend and philosophers pondered on it. The new belief was that natural sciences held the key to understanding and intellectual consciousness. In other words, science was 'in' and intuition was 'out'.

As sometimes happens with radical change, the pendulum at first swings too far in one direction. We still suffer from the intellectual snobbery and narrow-mindedness of that time.

What we need to aim for, as in all things, is moderation, or a balance of reason and intuition. We are coming round to this, but let's hope the pendulum doesn't swing so far the other way that we start to disregard science. I have always believed that science and intuition go hand-in-hand – the creative person's thoughts of today are the scientist's discoveries of tomorrow.

Today, because of the introduction in the last century of medicinal drugs, we have let our use of colour as a healing agent lapse. This is absurd, because how can we ignore the sun and its light? We are now beginning to remember and appreciate the greatness and influence that colour has on human affairs. The rainbow truly is smiling on the universe. The rainbow can be seen in so many things – water, snow crystals – it's reflected everywhere. Colour affects our emotions, which are shown through our bodies. Man does not have to see or feel colour to be affected by it. Our interest is now returning to the realm of light and it's showing us that all our ills are due to a lack of harmony with nature's laws. We have lost our focus and the only way back into well-being is to read the bible of light. Colour is the affirmation of light. Light is truly celestial medicine.

Colour is an intimate part of our being. The body acts as a prism in the light. When we are truly well, all the colours shine out from us in an ever-changing but always rhythmically serene lightshow. Then we are being the light we truly are to one another.

Colour is the simplest and most accurate therapeutic measure yet developed. It is nature's healer. It can be prescribed just as drugs can. Don't choose to be ill – choose a colour instead!

The application of various colours can affect health beneficially on all levels. This is the power of colour. Whether we realise it or not, colour has an energy that affects us physically (red), mentally (yellow) and emotionally (blue). Every emotion and feeling that we have is related to a particular colour. We get angry and 'see red', for instance. Sometimes the colour comes first – we see red and feel irritable and hot. Colour association is also attached to everything we do or have ever done in our lives, whether it be experience, behaviour, lessons we've learned or our surroundings. We can even chart a human lifetime by the colour-related phases of development, using the seven spectrum colours of the rainbow as a growth chart. The stages of man's growth pattern are related to the core meaning of each colour, as listed in the table below.

Birth to 10 years	RED	Physical expansion
10 to 15 years	ORANGE	Movement, dancing, athletics
15 to 20 years	YELLOW	Mental ability, education, study
20 to 40 years	GREEN	Relationships, love, children
40 to 60 years	BLUE	Transition from activity to contemplation
60 to 70 years	INDIGO	Perception – gathers together to make whole
70 years plus	PURPLE	Visionary – no limitations

As science has known for some time, everything in the universe is a certain combination of vibrations. All organs and parts of our bodies, when healthy, hold to a particular set of harmonious vibrations or, in musical terms, notes. From this point of view, we can be seen as marvellously complex and individual pieces of music. If we become ill or diseased, it means that disharmony has crept into the music – off-colour means off-key. Even thoughts and ideas are vibrations and can be as 'unwell' as the liver or pancreas or any other part of the body.

Colours affect man totally. Man uses colour as an experience of feeling. Colour has a quality of zinging out towards you. It vibrates and hums until it sings to you, rather like music, except that colour sings to the eye and not the ear.

Colour healing is a wonderfully direct way of working upon the body. Neither flesh nor mental attitude nor emotion are a barrier to colour. Colour can go to the seat of a problem instantly. We can eat, drink, breathe, visualise, meditate and dance colour. We absorb more colour when we are unwell and we can apply colour to restore the bank of health.

Each day we wake up to a world pulsating – sounds, sights and vibrations of all descriptions. Each day is new and different from the one before, changing constantly. But the one thing that never changes is the fact that colour is an integral part of this world. When we start to explore the world of colour, we realise there is more to colour than meets the eye. We experience a multitude of responses to colour all the time on a conscious and unconscious level. Colour is our universe. It affects everything that we touch, eat, drink, use and are surrounded by. Colour helps us delve into our history. Through colour we can move from the flower we are in the present to the roots beneath the earth of the past.

If we look back in time we can actually trace our evolution by looking at the colours that depicted that time. For instance, Stone Age people, 50,000 years ago, decorated their caves in Altimira in Spain with drawings of bears, bulls and other animals of that time. Prehistoric art in Africa, Europe and other parts of the world were concerned with physical survival. The colours used by the artists were very primitive. The dark reds show the physical hardship and brutality of that time, the hunting of flesh to survive. The ochres and dark oranges and blacks show the restrictions of the time. The brown earth indicates the great potential as yet untapped. These magnetic colours represent a way of life and an environment that was concerned with the physical.

Humanity has moved up the colour spectrum as the ages have passed. I believe that when humans started to domest-icate animals, and keep them captive for food in an enclosure rather than hunting for them, they were starting to work from the intellect and not from brawn. All through history the peck-ing order in society can be seen by the colour of the clothes worn. In Roman times thousands of snails had to be crushed to produce enough dye for the Emperor's purple robes – purple the leader, the ruler taking his own power. The poor were not allowed to wear colour. In Renaissance times, artists loved to use crushed crystals to make murals, crushed crystals having been used for their colour content for medicines centuries before. In Puritan times the predominant colour was grey. Grey slows things down and deprives. Grey is not into sexuality, and nor were the Puritans! Post-war Britain was a grey time, a time of austerity and criticism. My father, like all men of that time, would not have been seen dead without his grey suit. But grey is like a coat of armour, you can't move in it, which is exactly how the nation felt at that time. When times are prosperous and people are happy and feel like rejoicing, out come the bright colours. This has been shown throughout history as humans have discovered the magic of colour.

We now come to mankind in modern times – the Aquarian Age. The colour of today is blue. We are in the space age. The pace has quickened and we are moving faster. It is the age of the scientist, but science is combined with the higher spiritual self. In this new age we are seeking the truth. The one reason that may prevent mankind from being in the blue of truth is fear. Fear makes us walk backwards; it makes us contract. Fear will turn us away from the truth. Blue will not only help us to keep to the truth, it is also the great healer; the carer that combats pain, brutality and cruelty.

The use of colour is both an art and a science. The colour consultant combines knowledge, intuition and judgement. These are talents we all possess, and the information and exercises in the remainder of the book are directed to helping you develop those talents within yourself.

2

encountering colour

Favourite Colours

I am often asked the significance of a person's favourite colour. Does it automatically mean that it's the best colour for them? Is it their soul colour? The answer is no, not necessarily. Your favourite colour may not be the safest or the best colour for you to use for healing, but it will give clues about your life and circumstances. It could be a colour you are addicted to, conversely it could be your soul colour – the colour of whom you really are.

Some people say, 'I don't have a favourite colour', but you do, we all do. If you have difficulty in pinpointing a colour, think back to when you were a child or a teenager. Maybe you had a favourite gold-coloured teddy bear. Gold could be your colour, so use it as a key to unlock some clues about yourself.

At first I was hard pushed to come up with my own favourite colour – I seemed to like them all. Then I remembered as a child I had a dance costume that was cerise pink and I instantly knew that that was my favourite.

Colour Blindness and Blindness

Colour blindness affects males more than females, but is passed on from mother to son. You can be born with colour blindness or it can come about through disease, vitamin deficiency or exposure to a number of poisons. The person with congenital colour blindness will have a more serious defect in their vision. Their main difficulty is with differentiating between the shades. People who are colour blind from the other causes may only experience a dullness of colour.

Red and green are usually the two colours that help diagnose colour blindness. There is usually difficulty in differentiating between the two, although other combinations can also cause problems. Often there is an inability to separate light shades from dark.

I've often heard it said that a colour-blind person perceives colour on a different level – perhaps they do, but they certainly have difficulty in distinguishing one colour from another on an Earthly level! A person may not be aware of the defect in their vision until someone asks, 'Why are you wearing a red tie?' when they thought they were wearing a green one. There is no known cure for colour blindness as yet.

People who are blind have an understanding of colour through vibration. In some houses, the doors are painted different colours. The blind person can feel the door with their hands for the vibration and then will know where the door leads to. An experiment was done in America where coloured spots were placed on a table, and every time a blind person put their hand near a particular spot they could always tell the colour by the vibration they felt.

A Dislike of Colour: Colourphobia

I have come across a few people who actually dislike all colour – not a single colour appeals to them. When someone feels this way, what they are actually saying is that they don't like themselves. They feel life has not been very gracious to them. They believe it has given them a rough deal and as a consequence they have learned to hate it and themselves too, as well as colour.

A dislike for a particular colour is just as revealing as an attraction. The rejected colour represents a challenge, as it points to a deep inner need. It reveals what is holding you back, what the stumbling block is, even if you didn't know you were stumbling! Some aspect of the colour has a message for you, as you will discover in The Psychology of Colour chapter.

The Green of Money

THE COLOUR OF ABUNDANCE

Life is a continuing series of experiences which are rarely the same twice. There may be similar circumstances, but different players and logic. Money has the same patterning. It's always there, as life is; it just depends on whether you have it or not. It may have disappeared from your orbit at the moment, but nonetheless money can be brought back into your life if you persevere. It's important to explore why money seems elusive. It is necessary to get a grip and fathom out how money can be made to work for you instead of making you a victim.

Originally money was worth the amount of metal that was in it. An English silver shilling was worth one shilling of silver. A crash in silver prices in the late 19th century meant that from then on the metal in a shilling was worth less than the value of the coin. Paper money – the 'greenback' in the USA – was originally a written promise to whomever owned that piece of paper for a given amount of silver or gold. Modern money literally has no intrinsic value, yet it still retains its value of bargaining. What money represents today is *value*, the yellow attribute of green.

It is commonly believed that money represents freedom, the freedom of choice, and it does. First of all, to attain money you have to become a master of *valuation*. The money by itself represents nothing; it's how you *value* it, and the commodity you're after, that counts. For example, I own an apple, and you want it. I offer to sell it to you for ten pence. You may only value it at six pence. From then on we will negotiate its value in monetary terms, and barter until we come to an agreement on the coinage value of the fruit. Green is a combination of yellow and blue. The yellow energy that is in the colour green will have done its work. Yellow brings in your intellect which, combined with the blue in green, enables you to think before you act. When these two energies combine, the green vibration of money can come into play in a balanced way, full of prosperity and abundance.

BECOMING MONEY EFFECTIVE

Reverend Martin Luther King said that there are three conversions necessary: of the heart, the mind, and the purse. The last can seem the most difficult to achieve. Our parents originally set our attitudes to the green stuff. Sometimes parents find it as difficult a subject to talk to their children about as sex or death. If your parents have always said 'We can't afford it', then you will always regard the cup of life as half empty rather than half full. Schools also ignore the importance of money, rarely touching upon the subject, let alone giving education on how to manage it later on. It's said that a fool and his money are soon parted, which is true. What can separate you from your true abundance is ignorance. We have to be taught about money to be financially literate in the same way that we have to learn the alphabet to be able to read and write. It is important to examine what it is in ourselves that makes it difficult to attain money.

AM I A FINANCIAL WINNER OR LOSER?
Questionnaire: Victim or Victor?

This self-test is to determine how successful you are at attaining that pot of gold. Just answer yes or no to each question.

◆ Can I identify my preferred way of managing my money?
◆ Am I aware how money influences my life?
◆ Do I know how I spend all of my money?
◆ Can I use my money to clear any problems I have?
◆ Am I financially literate?
◆ Do I know how to enable money to work for me?
◆ Am I receiving payment for what I'm worth?
◆ Do I find it easy to ask for money due to me?
◆ Do I believe it's better to give than receive money?

Answer no to any of the above questions and you are deficient in handling your personal finances in a balanced way. Harsh as it may seem, money and emotions do not mix. Once you have acquired money by the rules of *valuation*, which will have necessitated using your mind and thinking, you can emotionally donate it wherever you wish.

Clearing the Mind and Emotions

Money issues can create the emotion of anxiety, causing stress, which in turn dams up the flow of abundance. A quick test is to put some coins and paper money into the palm of your left hand and feel the emotion you are experiencing. Be aware if you feel happy or depressed. Have a sense of your calmness, or lack of it, in your heart. If not, then you will work negatively with money energy at that moment, so it would be best not to negotiate that day! Take a deep breath in and slowly breathe out, releasing the dark green from your breath. Stress can be transformed into excitement, which leads to power.

PRESSURE STRESS RELEASE WITH THUMBWORK EXERCISE

To further release stress and anxiety, press three key points on top of your arm, using the thumb of your other hand (shown below).

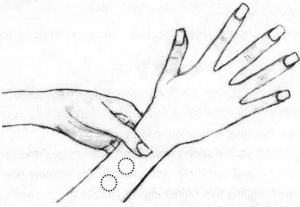

◆ The first point is located two inches from the wrist. The others are two inches apart.
◆ Rotate the thumb pad on each spot three times in small, clockwise circles.
◆ The thumb pressure massage will release stress and allow magnetic energy to flow.

INTUITIVE MENTAL ABUNDANCE EXERCISE

This exercise helps you to delve into your subconscious mind to see how you intuitively relate to money.

◆ Colour in the three squares below in order, and write three words next to each coloured square.
◆ Do not read The Psychology of Colour chapter to find an interpretation until you have completed the exercise:

1 ☐ _Calm beauty outgoing_

2 ☐ _Enhancing healing peace_

3 ☐ _Excitement energy fun_

Interpretation

The colours chosen represent your emotional attitude to money.

◆ The colour of square 1 shows how you think you behave with money, and the three words which follow show how you are handling that colour-energy vibration.
◆ The second square shows how others witness you managing money, and the three words which follow show how you are handling that colour-energy vibration.

◆ The third shows how you would like to deal with abundance and money success, and the three words which follow show how you are handling that colour-energy vibration.

Be glad and generous in your heart to yourself and with others. This allows you to be all-loving and giving.

Colour and Your Clothes

THE COLOURS THAT YOU WEAR ARE YOUR OWN PERSONAL CALLING CARD

There has long been an awareness of the impact colour in fashion makes upon the public, particularly in industry and marketing. However, we also need to become aware of the messages and signals that the clothes we are wearing send out. All colours have changing characteristics and affect not only us but the people we come into contact with. Thus it is extremely important that we are conscious of the colours we choose. The body actually absorbs little of the colour-vibration from our clothes. The real impact is on our psyche through our eyes – which in turn creates a marked difference in our emotions and moods.

So why are we drawn to certain colours and not others? We are attracted because, on a certain level within us, we need that particular colour's vibration to correct an imbalance in our systems, be it mental, physical or spiritual. Often, for the very reason that we are unbalanced, we tend to choose the colours that support the imbalance, rather than those that address the disturbance. It's very much like the nervous wanting a cigarette, or being depressed through drugs or alcohol. Fortunately this pattern can be broken with colour, through the use of turquoise and blue, which gently calm the system. Indigo can then be used to provide support for relief of the addictive patterns themselves.

Colour helps us delve into our history. It is possible to use colour to travel back through our lives to remember what was happening to us at any given time. If you are unable to recall the events in your life when you were a certain age, just recall which colour you favoured in clothing at that time. This will give valuable clues as to your motivations and state of being at that period – read The Psychology of Colour chapter for interpretation. For example, if a person wore a lot of blue in their middle teens it shows that, on a hindrance level, they were stuck in a rut. But it also shows that the person had blue's patience in accepting that which could not be changed, and, by examining the truth of it, there was an opportunity to bring about its own healing. This would have enabled the person to become free to move on.

Before you invest in expensive items of clothing it is a good idea to learn the language of colour! The visual effect of trendy fashion is usually the goal, completely ignoring the vibrational health and healing qualities of its colours, so think colour healing before you buy. How many times have you chosen an item of clothing one day, and the next morning realised that it's the last thing you want to wear? It seemed perfect at the time, but somehow overnight it isn't! The answer is that your body's chemistry has changed during sleep, so your vibrational needs for colour are now different: unmet colour needs can compel us to make unnecessary, and expensive, purchases. So, if finances are a little short and you absolutely *must* have that costly flaming red sweater you've just seen, buy a red light bulb, take it home, and sit in its glow for 20 minutes. Suddenly you may find that you've lost that compelling urge to purchase the sweater

– because you've given yourself the colour's healing tonic your body or psyche was asking for. And you've also saved a lot of money!

CHOOSING COLOURS FOR SPECIFIC EFFECTS

There are unlimited combinations of colours available so you can enhance your life by the clothes you put on.

◆ Remember when grouping colours together, the dominant hue will direct and focus your system.

◆ Be aware of the need for balance, so do not overload with a colour because you think it will help you feel better. Just wear it one day at a time. If there is no improvement after seven days, leave it for a week and try again.

◆ If you sense that a certain colour has overloaded you, wear something green for a day to neutralise the effect.

◆ Sometimes there is a colour you can't stand, but you realise it will be of benefit. Wear it hidden as underwear, and your body will respond to its vibration anyway.

◆ Combining many colours in an outfit is not recommended if you are seeking the healing benefits of what you are wearing. No more than three colours is best for health, having first selected them for their specific benefits. Any more than that dissipates their healing qualities, although for a general tonic, a medley of colours can be enjoyed for up to eight hours at a time, but not on consecutive days. Three times in a week is about right.

◆ Regard coloured clothes as ingredients and be selective. Use colour to aid and abet you in your daily endeavours.

BENEFICIAL SUGGESTIONS

◆ Orange can be worn to combat fear and grief, blues for the release of stress, and red to boost sluggish circulation. Your great-grandparents knew the value of red flannelette night-wear to harness its hot vibration to keep warm.

◆ Going to the bank for a loan? A sombre grey is perfect. Banks always say hooray for grey! Add the colour green for money – very impressive.

◆ Do you need to make an impact with your clothes at an interview? Need to appear bright and alert? Add a little gold and yellow to show that you are trustworthy, and can come up with interesting ideas!

◆ Are you looking to employ somebody who will be a support, and content to be in the wings and hold the fort for you? Then hire anyone wearing brown immediately!

◆ Are you nervous at lecturing or speaking in front of a crowd? Then conceal turquoise about your person to steady and calm you.

The age a colour is worn can be an important indication of where the person is in themselves. Pink and black are good examples. When a young female wears pink it shows she is ready to develop her full potential; but in a mature woman of 50 plus, it means it is reassessment time – and, if necessary, a time to dissolve away old ideas and issues.

Teenagers in black leather are stating that they are ready to take control and run the world, believing they can do a better job of making the universe work than their pre-decessors did. They are no longer willing to let their parents, or society, tell them what to do. In the 20s and 30s, black worn obsessively indicates that something has brought the person's life to a halt, put it on hold. They feel boxed in. By the time we pass 40, how we relate to black shows how we have come to terms with power and control. In general, if assessing anyone wearing black, see if there is another colour with it. This will show physiologically what the person's expectations will be. And, if the boss is wearing a black suit with a pink shirt or tie, then watch to see who is about to get fired!

Décor for Health and Well-being

Colours surround us all the time, in homes, offices, factories, schools, shopping centres, public buildings and so on. Colour and its messages lead us into every corner of the universe. What better way is there than to harness its mysteries, benefits and strengths than to enhance our environment at home, work and play? Light and colour are crucial to our health and well-being. Nature and its colours have the answers, and by learning nature's lessons we can continue its power and presence in our everyday life.

The colours in our environment can have a great effect on us. They can lift our spirits or depress us; they can speed us up or slow us down; they can soothe or irritate. Colour surrounds us at each and every moment, awake or asleep. Even things as simple as changing a baby's blanket from a stimulating colour to a soothing colour will affect their sleep. Changing wall colours at home can change the mood, and the habitability, of a room. In the workplace, colour can have a dramatic effect on the whole working environment.

For instance, it was found that painting stairways red will stop people idling for a chat. The red vibrations keep them moving. In the USA, managers were faced with the problem of their male employees spending too much time in the restroom (the loo in the UK) so they decided to paint the walls in the gents a sizzling electric green – no one hangs around in there now! In a lipstick factory it was discovered that the women working there were being over-exposed to red.

Absenteeism was high because of headaches and migraines. But painting the walls green counteracted the effect of the red and the headaches disappeared.

Colour consultants play a crucial role in creating safety colours for children's clothing, walkers and cyclists, colours that stand out in poor lighting conditions. In psychology, great strides have been made in the diagnosis and treatment of certain mental conditions through colour. Tests of colour preference have been created that reveal personal attributes useful in determining where that person's talents may be most successfully applied. Colour consultants have revolutionised hospitals, clinics and other places of healing through advising on the choice of appropriate colours. For instance, too much white in hospitals should be avoided as this will give a sterile feeling causing frustration. Pastels are better. Lavender is discovered to be a good colour to help eliminate anaesthetics or for anyone who is ill or convalescing. Surgeons wear dark green gowns in the operating theatre. Dark green has been proved to help staunch the flow of blood. First-aid kits are usually dark green too. And if you are visiting someone in hospital, give a thought to the flowers you take. Don't take red flowers which say 'get up and go', particularly if they've just had an operation.

OTHER DÉCOR COLOUR DISCOVERIES

Airports have neutral colours with bold red signs for directions. It's best not to use yellow in an aeroplane as this will cause nausea, but used in classrooms yellow will focus the concentration and stimulate the intellect. Primrose can be used for children at exam time – it helps their confidence and focuses the mind. A stronger yellow also helps with elimination – if they feel constipated because they are sitting down and not getting enough exercise!

The best colours in assembly halls or conference centres are the sombre, dignified colours such as dark blue and indigo which encourage structure and planning. In cafés, reds and oranges are the best colours to ensure that customers don't linger too long over a cup of coffee. These colours make you eat more quickly so it will certainly help speed up the turnover. A survey was conducted on colouring prison cells pink to quieten the inmates. I saw this on television and I thought 'They won't be quiet for long, there's too much red in it,' when the prison orderly said, 'But after an hour they were fighting again!' They needed more white in the pink to keep them contented. Football crowds flooded with yellow were found to get very disruptive and hostile and angry. Pale blue would have been better. Some prisons have discovered that using a mild pink for short periods reduces tension and disturbances. But, it must be very pale: too much red in it can rebound and cause disruptions. Autistic children who have a problem with communication have been found to respond well to peach and the social colour orange.

How effective colour can be in schools is demonstrated by a teacher who had problems with an unruly class at morning assembly. While still in the classroom, the teacher had the class imagine an opening in the tops of their heads, and a beautiful turquoise light flowing in. The class not only loved it, they were well-behaved in the assembly – and the teacher was summoned by the headmaster to explain the dramatic turn-around in their behaviour!

In law courts the surroundings are usually mature brown wood which gives a feeling of solidity. The jury room has blue carpet, blue being the colour of thinking and contemplation. The judge is often red robed and surrounded by red carpet. He is going to put into action the outcome of a case.

Even the colours of flags are reflective of the nation they represent. India, for instance, has orange, white and green as its national colours. The white stands for interests in all walks of life, the green to aim for balance in the country's economics, and the orange counteracts the anaemia that afflicts the people. The colour of the flag has given us the country's domestic condition.

COLOURING THE MOOD OF YOUR HOME

Décor in the home is of a profound significance. The colour schemes we use can alter the amount and type of light our skin tissues and internal organs receive. Light is known to be a most important influence affecting our bodily functions.

Poor colour schemes in the home can not only shock the eyes, but can also cause discomfort and fatigue. With a little time and care, colour can be used to produce an atmosphere rich in comfort, joy and happiness. Your own unique personality is the key to your choice in décor. A quiet person trying to use stimulating colours just because it seems the done thing will wind up having difficulty living in their own home. It is *you* who ultimately has to live with your chosen colour scheme, so never choose a colour just because it is fashionable.

The size and shape of a room are important considerations in colour choice. A strong colour in a small room causes it to close in on itself, making it claustrophobic. Small rooms look spacious decorated in single light colours; dark, narrow rooms need light, clear colours. Colours also become more intense in large rooms than in small. Darker ceilings or carpets shorten walls, whereas paler colours open up a room. If you are painting just one wall in a different colour, avoid using it on a wall where there is a door or window. This dissipates the colour energy. Dark colours which look good with bright sunlight on them will be several shades duller at night in electric light. At the other end of the scale, an overdose of white can be tiring for the eyes and cause frustration, so check how much daylight a room gets before using white.

Use beige virtually anywhere, but remember it needs another strong colour or two with it, although no more than two. Red, orange, and yellow – the strong, expansive colours – have an immediate impact upon the eye and make the space active. Blue, indigo, and purple – the contra-active colours – quieten energies, and cool and calm down interiors. A useful general rule is to keep all the hot colours, red, orange and yellow, for downstairs; use the cooler colours, blues to purples, for bedrooms and bathrooms upstairs.

Entrance Hallways

Hallways give the first impression of our personality and home environment. Use the welcoming, warmer colours here, such as corals and peaches. Blue and turquoise feed the nervous system, and create a tranquil atmosphere.

Yellow-decorated halls show that the family would prefer to keep you there, talking, rather than taking you into the rest of the house. A brown hallway says enter, but don't plan on staying long. Creative occupants are reflected in white and purples: the design and effect of their homes are important to them. There will be few if any children here, but there may be a Siamese cat eyeing you up! Hallways decorated in green show that the family may not be too tidy – they usually have a love of the outside as well as animals.

Kitchen

Kitchens are busy places, and regarded by many as the very heart of the home. Do not use blues or purples here, as these colours have a slowing-down effect, just when you need to get busy! Terracotta and orange are perfect because they promote action and activity. Bright green encourages wonderfully healthy goodness to be conjured up, and yellow is a very good colour as it stimulates the intellect, helping you to concentrate on the job at hand. Use red sparingly, as it can become a bit claustrophobic.

Dining Rooms

Restaurants have discovered that when the décor includes white and brown, people's appetites are heartiest and the most food is eaten. The brown links physically to nature: the brown earth where food grows, allowing the digestion to work well under brown's steady influence. White is connected to the mother and therefore mother's milk, the original source of nourishment and comfort. To encourage genial conversation add a touch of turquoise to the décor; or you can add turquoise-highlighted plates, glasses, napkins or flowers. You can bring in other colours to add further dimensions to the meal: blue, indigo and purple for a dinner to be lingered over, or red, orange and yellow to speed up the proceedings.

The Living Room

Although colour enables you to stamp your own indelible mark, account must be taken of the effect colour has on others who will be using the area. Spaces used by the entire family, like the living room, are where each individual can express themselves. For these rooms it's best to choose colours that suit your family's widest needs.

Choosing the correct colour surrounds the occupants with the colour's influences in the room. For example, families prone to arguments need a nice rich blue in the room to calm and relax the atmosphere. If you are a highly sociable family and have lots of family gatherings or friends around, then having yellow on the walls keeps the conversation flowing, loosens the tongue and encourages fun and laughter. If you move to the living room after meals, a strong green will aid digestion, but do not have everything green in this room, as too much exposure to green creates a soporific atmosphere, eventually leading to depression.

Bedrooms

A bedroom is a place of relaxation and refreshment, so use all the blues, plus lavender, lilac and violets. Red and orange in the bedroom tends to be overstimulating, resulting in sleeplessness. Use indigo for insomnia; and indigo is also a useful bedroom colour if you suffer from migraines or headaches. Introduce a little gold to allow the occupant to surrender to a good night's restful bliss. For different moods, use different coloured light bulbs, night attire and coloured sheets. For example, roses or removable red ornaments can be used to revitalise a slow sex life – just to start off activities. Check The Psychology of Colour chapter for further ideas.

Children's Bedrooms

Too many colours in a child's bedroom overwhelm, and will keep a child awake. Keep it simple and use no more than three colours. Both ends of the spectrum should be present among the walls, carpet or furnishings. The child usually has different-coloured toys to bring in the extra colours, so a cool, pale apple green is appropriate. Primrose yellow walls benefit the older child studying for exams – to encourage and help the intellect to concentrate on the work at hand. Yellow also allows a flow of energy, stopping the child from feeling stuck and bogged down with too much study.

Bathrooms

The bathroom is where we go to cleanse and refresh, ready-ing ourselves to start all over again. Use your bathroom as your own personal sanctuary from the stresses and pressures of modern life. Water is a great healer. Add dark green plants to the room to detoxify the body, along with dark green or yellow candles. Turn the bathwater turquoise with bubble bath, enabling you to concentrate only on yourself at this precious time. Create a real haven – an exotic bird-of-para-dise bathroom with all colours of the rainbow, using jungle-printed paper or tiles depicting butterflies, birds and flowers. Add sea shells to a blue bathroom to create both relaxation and a sense of swimming in healing waters. To avoid an over-load of colour, incorporate plain white to give a breathing space. Use hot colours for large families where time needs to be allocated.

A plain white bathroom can become a healing temple by using coloured lights or accessories for specific healing, such as orange for the alleviation of rheumatoid arthritis. Even indigo-coloured towels are useful for the relief of hangovers! Refer to Chapter 5 for colour-healing suggestions.

Why not give yourself a floral healing bath? Flowers are a particularly beautiful way to infuse colour. Caress the flower in your hands, and then transfer your hands containing the blos-som into the water. The flower's colour will infuse the bath with colour-energy. You may also wish to add the perfume fragrance of flowers to the water to give extra healing.

Basements

Basements can be dark, musty and depressing because of little light. The best colour to use is white, which will reflect, widen and lighten the surroundings. If there are pipes surrounding the walls, paint these all the colours of the rainbow, turning them into splendid features instead of ugly eyesores. Then, paint cupboards or any odd shapes with exquisite bright colours and let them sing out to you with fun and joy.

The Garden

We are nearer to God's love when we stroll in our parks or gardens than anywhere else on Earth. The splendour of nature's magnificence is a miracle to behold. The ancients worshipped the sun, for without that all life ceased; the sun's rainbow can be seen in so many things: water, flowers, crystals and snow.

Gardens can be designed specifically for healing. The blue sky is already there, reflecting the colour signifying the healer. The green colour of grass has powerful qualities for strengthening the physical body, and it can detoxify a clogged-up system. The trees' brown trunks remind us of the dark depths of Earth's potential, with multicoloured fruits nestling in the tree's green leaves. To sit under a tree is to connect yourself at all levels to nature's healing force: hug and embrace a tree, or put your back against its bark and gently rub your spine up and down, to generate nature's life energy.

But dark grey paving stones, cement or concrete can put a garden's healing energy on hold and restrict. It's better to have terracotta bricks, multicoloured stone or natural wood, which blends in with the outdoor surroundings, and boosts the natural colour energies.

When a garden is barren in the winter, lay clusters of coloured crystals or stones on the flower beds, or even hang them from bare stems and bushes to give a show of colour-energy. You can paint your dull garden shed yellow, or gold and white; garden benches can also be painted wonderful colours. A splendid orange encourages the spirits and warms the heart and soul – it stands out wonderfully against the background of dormant brown earth in a cold climate. Line up brightly coloured flower pots on a window ledge in all the colours of the rainbow to give healing every time you see them through your window.

Instead of choosing your home environment's colours haphazardly, use colour as a cosmic tuning fork. It can create tranquillity and harmony.

ENHANCING THE MOOD OF YOUR OFFICE

Balanced use of colour in offices has emerged as a vital means of comfort for employees as well as increased productivity for business. It is important to be aware that improperly applied colour can interfere with and distract from work. Colour is an effective means of changing the dynamics of an environment.

Management Offices

Executive offices need to present an aura of leadership and direction: a rich purple carpet sends the message of big ideas and creativity, along with luxury. Trust and loyalty are emphasised through gold décor. The addition of green plants stresses money and balance.

Open-Plan Offices

Many people sharing the same large space presents problems. Because of the territorial nature of human beings, productivity-sapping anxiety occurs when personal space is encroached. Where offices solve this through dividers, colour is an important factor in their effectiveness. Individual colours enhance the feeling of personal space, and a colour appropriate to the task at hand can enhance productivity, lifting the spirit.

Browns and dark greens create isolation and sap morale. Make the overall décor a basic cream, then introduce some bright colours for the paintwork such as orange, emerald green, rose and rich blue. If only one colour is possible use a bright turquoise – this creates the necessary feeling of privacy. Employees can then introduce their own personal colours in their spaces, using ornaments or flowers.

High Finance
For offices buzzing with high pressure activities, like sales and the stock market, energetic colours, such as red-covered upholstery, are needed. This adds zest, energy and drive, literally putting workers in the hot seat! Green walls and carpets are a good balance to the red and reduce headaches that occur because of work pressure.

Office at Home
Keeping personal life separate from work is often the greatest challenge of working at home. Keep the business in the office space where it belongs through the use of royal blue carpets, yellow curtains and pale blue or primrose-yellow walls.

In General
On the whole, it's best to avoid white offices. Because it contains all colours, there is very little stimulus from white. With long exposure it tends to create irritability, reducing productivity. Brown is also a poor colour, creating tiredness and non-productivity – a closing-up of energies. Grey colours can result in melancholy, and black restricts movement, keeping everything on hold. Always use another colour with beige. Alone it creates negativity.

Wherever the office is located, and whatever function it performs, don't forget details like stationery: its colours make a statement about the business. For example, it's best to abandon classic white paper: it can cause distraction from the written word. By carefully considering the company's desired image, and referring to The Psychology of Colour chapter, you can create an appropriate colour message for your company's letter head or logo. The colour vibration you send out into the world can, in a subtle way, influence the productivity and success of the company, benefiting everyone – from the board-room to the employee to the public.

3

therapeutic colour

Healing Yourself

It was Hippocrates who said he would rather know what sort of person has a disease than what sort of disease a person has. The first step towards healing is to be able to recognise patterns in our life that we act out. You are constantly living it if you don't relive it. To relive it you must experience the original pain. You have to get to the root cause. What we mean by this is if you are to become well, you have to relive your past hurts so you can release them. This is done in therapy or just by talking it through with a friend. If you don't do this, you will experience the pain every day until you do face up to it and relive it.

If you always do what you've always done, you'll always get what you've always got. People are generally what they think themselves to be. What is healing anyway? Is it just curing an organ in the body or making the person's life better? When you become ill you don't believe in a future, and when you don't have a future you don't take care of yourself.

Sometimes it is necessary to look at what the illness is, to look into the illness rather than be limited by the usual preconception of it. When we get flu, for instance, we expect to have a temperature for several days, feel off-colour then suffer from catarrh, and so on. This is our preconception about what flu is. However, we could look at the reason *why* we have it, what was the emotional cause. 'Why did *I* get flu? Why was I vulnerable to it? Many other people around me could have got it but didn't. Why me?' They didn't get it because their emotional make-up, particular personal pattern, didn't fit the energy pattern of the flu.

Once we have recognised the patterns in our life, both positive and negative, we will have to get behind them to find the person we truly are. Then we will have to see why we adopted the patterns or the role in the first place and what function they serve in the present. Usually, the reason why we adopted the role in the first place was fear. Peace of mind sends the body a 'live' message, while turmoil, conflict, fear and depression give it a 'die' message. When we lose connection with our inner self we lose connection with the outside world. What we create within will always be reflected without. Illness is seen as an imbalance of the forces within us. The only way to get out of our disharmonious state is by self-knowledge. This self-knowledge is available to us by several means, i.e. personal growth, which is the discovery of how we become motivated which will show us who we really are.

Regard your pains as a treasured wound. You either learn from them or you treasure them as a means to manipulate other people.

Disease is war. It is you at war with yourself. Fighting with ourselves within causes war to break out – we get ill. Fighting with ourselves weakens our immune system. Disease is regarded as an enemy. The best way to destroy the enemy is to make it your friend. It can become your *best* friend. Disease is telling you the truth about yourself. It means that you have ignored the whisper; now your body will make itself heard by a loud shout called disease.

Healing aims for the union of self with the sound within. We think our body is silent, but it's not. Even when we sit still, our body is full of sounds and rhythms. It is very noisy. Taking your pulse is listening to your internal sound. When I listen to my pulse I am listening to myself. Each of us is a symphony of thought, form, colour.

To heal ourselves we need to follow the thought-form-colour pattern being played within our body. Dancing also connects you to your own internal rhythms. The heartbeat is time and the circulation is space. The body has rhythm and it beats to the melody of the heart. That's why dance and movement are natural healers.

When you start to resonate with your self, you start to resume responsibility. Then you begin to have an influence on what is happening in your life. Only then can you be there for others as a healer.

Look to the kingdom in your own heart, your own personal kingdom where you rule supreme. Look for the gold that lies there within your own heart. When you are content within yourself you will be free of the dark yellow of judgement and condemnation. Being in this healing space takes total accept-ance of what is, which neutralises negative conditions. When you work with the gold of the heart, you are saying to the person who needs healing, and this may be yourself, 'I may not love what you do, but I love you anyway.'

Healing Others

As a healer, you can give through yourself and not of yourself. I remember an American woman at a lecture by a famous healer asking, 'How can I be a healer?'

The reply was, 'You must open your heart, not think of yourself, and become humble.'

'How do I do that?' she said.

'You must not be selfish,' came the reply.

The woman looked perplexed. I spoke to her afterwards. 'When you've got your heart open and there is this great big space,' I asked, 'what are you going to put in it first?'

She said she had no idea.

'Yourself,' I said, 'because if you don't, you will not be able to get rid of all your negative ways, thoughts and hang-ups. You must be selfishly there for *you* first. Otherwise you will be too busy using your energy to shore up your lack of self-esteem and low self-worth. Of course your heart will be closed while you have to do this, and rightly so.'

Turquoise is the colour to help you focus on yourself. Only when you have put yourself in that healing space of the open heart and seen to your needs can your heart then be free for anybody else.

The gold of self-trust is crucial to the development of independence, and for healing. It opens up the heart. When I vibrate to the gold of trust within my psyche, then I can surrender. Trusting does not mean that I become a victim. It means whatever the world may throw at me, or put my way, I will have the confidence to deal with it come what may.

True healing takes place through the heart. When you can let go of the holding of the mind you can discover the healing of the body. As Dylan Thomas' poem about his father's death puts it, we 'do not go gently into that good night'. We have great anger at 'the dying of the light', i.e. our own death.

When a person is very ill or in crisis, they sometimes ask, 'Will I live or die?' Only the heart can answer. Being in the heart is not about living or dying, but focusing on the moment to look beyond the mind and body and take a step into the unknown, which allows the present to be experienced fully and naturally. Healing doesn't necessarily mean being physically cured – sometimes it is healing into death. We all look for a way to conquer death. The yogis of ancient times were said to have found a way, but it did not mean they would live physically forever. To have conquered death is when a person decides for themselves the right time to depart from this Earth – to decide consciously 'I will now leave my body,' instead of being forced earlier than expected because of circumstances or disease.

To be in the heart is to be able to focus on the moment and look without fear beyond the mind into the unknown. When we can take the step of allowing ourselves to be in the state of healing, we allow ourselves to become whole again. There is a risk however. Are we going to be healed into bodily health, or healed into the next realm? Healing is taking the future into our hands. Something within the heart touches the disease and allows it to depart and wholeness to return.

Being in the healing space requires total acceptance of the problem. This is what neutralises and dissolves the negative factor. It is not necessary to appear spiritual – just to *be* it. God appears in many guises.

As I said before, when we go to a therapist we are asking for support or assistance. We may not be consciously aware that this puts us in a state of humility, which allows us to be teachable. When we are teachable, we are ready to learn and grow. We tend to think that a therapist's support is going to be nice, orderly and comfortable. But support can also seem unreal, uncomfortable and unexpected. A therapist can help all aspects come together, which may act as a trigger to move energy forward.

It is important to realise that the therapist is not perfect. No one is perfect; no one can be put on a pedestal. What we have to realise is that there is no formula for life; there are no guarantees, even in therapy.

I believe it is important that a therapist/healer has been, or still is, in therapy themselves. After all, it could become difficult if the client is constantly pressing the buttons connected to your unresolved issues. When I am teaching, or with a client, I often wonder who is the healer here and who is the client?

His Holiness Param Sant put what healing work is all about very neatly: 'Because I give positive thoughts with a clear conscience, people have faith that whatever I say will happen. Thus, their faith works and they give credit to me, while I do nothing. I simply transform the negative into a positive. This is what I do.' This is a reminder of who we are as healers.

Colour and the Self

Colour is a non-invasive means of discovering your true self. Colour is the yellow brick road into the realm of childhood past – and, often, even further back. It can open the door to your childhood, a door that has been kept closed to the conscious mind all the years since.

Colour has the ability, if you learn its language, to tell you how life really was for you at any time in your past.

HOW COLOUR CAN HEAL YOUR INNER CHILD
A young child is pure essence. When we do not get the kind of loving attention we expect and need as a child, its absence

hurts us. This is to say nothing of the effect that the presence of the negative attention of angry words, indifference and beatings has. The child is perfect – nothing changes that. It is only the stuff others put into the child, or what the child takes, that leads us falsely to identify that child differently or as something less.

At first we have no defence against this hurt, but we soon begin to create one. We put a shell around our essential self. But things often turn into their opposites in psychological matters, which is why, in our adult self, this childhood shell becomes a hollow, unreal self inside which our child essence is no longer defended but imprisoned.

The major work of what is known as 'self-growth' is to dissolve this castle that has become a prison, and release its small prisoner. Quite often it begins to crumble from the passage of time without any conscious work by the person concerned – or even any understanding of what is going on.

The child within us is a very real person, and we should treat it as such. A therapist I was working with taught me this in one short sentence.

I had had a dream in which my inner child appeared, crying inconsolably and looking uncared for and dirty. It was very hard for my mother to keep us clean in the wartime, even though she was almost paranoid about cleanliness. There was no such thing as hot running water. We were lucky to get water to drink, let alone to have a bath, which in our house was probably full of bricks from the bomb-damaged walls, anyway. 'How can I possibly cuddle and love that little child when it's so dirty and it smells?' I asked my therapist. She turned round to me and said, 'Well, give it a wash.'

I hadn't thought of that. I'd forgotten that I could now parent my inner child the way it had never been parented. The idea that the child we once were might still be trying to complete its growth may seem strange at first glance. However, many people have discovered, with the aid of the many kinds of therapy (colour included) and personal growth techniques, that it is true. We can be fully grown physically and yet not have completed the stages of emotional and mental growth that are needed to become adults.

We hold our own child, the child we once were, within us until the day we die. Our child contains many children within it. Each phase of our childhood will be a different child. Our reaction to life as an adult will be at least partly determined by that little child. It holds the keys to the patterns of our relationships with each other and with the world.

If our child was unloved or abused in any way, that inner child will, even though we are now adults, seek fulfilment of its unsatisfied needs from our present partner. This will be true of not just our love partners but also of our business, work and social partners. Unfortunately, it is not possible or appropriate for our partners to fill this old gap. Only we can.

Now, as adults, we can be the parent, or parents, our inner child never had, and give it what it never got and still seeks: the kind of parenting that will allow it to grow through each stage of its development correctly.

Accepting our child just as it is, and then giving it the parenting it needs, allows us to complete our growth. We cease being a victim to it. We do need to parent ourselves appropriately, of course. So often as adults we parent our own inner child the way we were parented – and sometimes our own children as well – which then continues the problem into the next generation.

However, this coin has another side too: we must release our parents from us, from our old resentments and accusations, in order to become good parents ourselves. We have to sever the cord. This is not so easy. Many people have claims upon their parents that they are unwilling to surrender. The difficulty is that often we are completely unaware that we have such claims. Some people want to stay a dependent child for instance. It is as though the person decided: 'It's better to have a connection through dependency than no connection at all.'

In a very real way, the child we once were and the parents we once had are still back 20, 30, 40 years ago, still caught in whatever painful events they had to live through together at the time. And tremors from those events and that relationship reach us every day, no matter what the distance is in time. Clients often make a statement along the lines of: 'Well, my childhood was difficult and there's nothing I can do about it.' They are quite often drawn to dark blue which, in its negative form, is saying 'I am the victim of my childhood'.

It may be true that we cannot change what happened to us: what was done was done and cannot be undone. But there is no point in blaming our parents. They were parenting the only way they knew how. However, though we may not be able to change the circumstances or the event itself, we can certainly discharge the emotional energy still held in the memory of the event. It is this undischarged energy – the grief, desolation, anger, fear or helpless resentment – that keeps seeping through or boiling up into our lives and bedevilling all our relationships, health and happiness. Until the charge is released, the event is energetically incomplete for us. It is, in effect, still happening. Once this energy is gone, the event becomes history. What happened in the past loses its power to cripple our present. We will be able to remember the event, but there will be no pain in it for us.

Colour is one way to let light into these incomplete times of childhood. Colour can also help to complete them, the balance restored and the person allowed to have the exhilarating experience of finding themselves free to live their lives in a present no longer haunted by the past.

WHEN BEING YOURSELF MEANS GIVING BACK WHAT WAS NEVER YOURS

The child we once were still lives in us. But so, also, does its mother – and what happened between them 20, 30, 40 years ago is still happening. My experience has been that using colour means it is not always necessary to re-live all the pain of a traumatic birth or a grievous childhood. The healing colour vibration will penetrate space and time. If that sounds like magic, it is probably because it is.

One day when I was in my forties, I woke up feeling terribly agitated. It stayed with me all morning. It was an intense edginess, as though I was about to go on stage, and it was most uncomfortable. About midday, I suddenly recognised where I had felt it before: I used to get it as a child.

The thought came to me, sit down and ask: 'Does this state belong to my inner child?' I sat down, closed my eyes, and I quietly went back through the years. I asked her, 'Did you ever feel the way I feel now?' The answer was 'Yes', it had also been her experience. Gradually I realised it was how I used to feel every day of my life as a child. I had got it from my mother. Nowadays, it would probably be called an anxiety neurosis.

Between the stress and uncertainty of war and all that she had to contend with from my father, my mother lived every day in a state of total anxiety. A young child has no choice but to learn from its mother; so from mine I could not help but learn anxiety. What about didn't matter: I existed, therefore I was anxious.

This was a revelation to me – not that my mother had been anxious, that I knew. What I had not known was that the feeling I had was her anxiety, and that I had taken it on long ago. I had learned it from her. Having realised this I could let my inner child know that being in a state of anxiety was not necessary to her survival; it was simply something she had learnt from her mother. I also realised that knowing this fact alone would not be enough: I had to get the energy of the anxiety out of my system in some way. I remembered a process I had intuitively discovered years before when I was having trouble releasing past hurts from my family. It will work for you too.

Healing Process: Root Colour Removal

◆ Sit in front of a mirror and open your mouth. Imagine a root that goes right down your throat, right down your gullet, way, way down deep.

◆ This is where the attachment lies, the root of the anxiety neurosis. Visualise the colour of the root. In my case was a pale primrose yellow – yellow often indicates mother issues.

◆ Open your mouth wide, and with both hands pull the root up and up ... and out of your mouth.

◆ Then, put it in the palm of your right hand where it now looks very deflated and crumpled. Lift your hand up in the air, and offer it back to your mother, or to whomever the attachment goes. It is their attachment, not yours.

◆ Then, thank the person very much for it, but tell them that you don't need it now and, as it doesn't belong to you, you are giving it back to them. Do this by visualising the person in your imagination, of course.

- If they have already passed on, death is no barrier to the effectiveness of such a process.
- Then, with your left hand, reach up. Above is an emerald green pot of balm being placed in your left hand. Emerald is connected to heart, pain and relationships. There is no colour in the balm itself; it is from the brilliance (see Chapters 5 and 7), from the clear light that all colours are held within.
- Scoop out the balm with your right hand and spread it all over your heart area and solar plexus, and on all the areas from which the roots have been wrenched. Feel it melt away into your body like a golden dew.
- Then, give the pot back.
- To check the meaning of the root colour you see in the process, go to the section in Chapter 7 on the psychology of colour.

Many of life's issues are connected to our mothers. Mothers have the greatest responsibility for moulding the human race. History and scriptures have always pointed this out, but we rarely bother to learn from them. A newborn child is influenced by the woman who gives birth to him or her. The mental state of the child is open and clear. It receives impressions and suggestions very easily. Its life will be formed by these primary impressions. The mother's role is not limited to feeding; with love she also imparts positive and constructive impressions. These are the key to the child's success in later life.

The Golden Tears of Forgiveness

Life is a school, and a hard school at that, and whoever we meet during this learning period of a 'life span' acts as a mirror encouraging us to see in ourselves that which we need to know in order to progress.

I remember being eight years old and looking at my parents and thinking, 'They're so young and scared'. They were like children and I felt so old by comparison. I was full of compassion and wanted to comfort them as they naïvely struggled with life.

Since that time, I have come to understand from my own researches and experiences that I chose my parents before I was born, just as we all do. This is called Karma (see Chapter 9). I can see now that they gave me the perfect soil in which to grow and learn my life's lessons – if I chose to do so. They were my perfect teachers, the two people who would give me exactly the environment I needed to develop and become whole in this lifetime.

It is only recently that I have completed the particular lesson that my parents embodied for me, which is that of the golden tears of forgiveness. Forgiveness does not mean that what has happened to you is all right. It wasn't then and it isn't now and never will be. Forgiveness means to have no energy still attached to what happened to you. You have no need to get even or resolve it. Forgiveness means there is no longer any anger or pain connected to it.

Forgiveness is the vehicle for correcting misconceptions. When we forgive, we let go of resistance which is fear, and give ourselves and others the opportunity to flow and move on. It is difficult to forgive and love others when we have not let go of the pain and hurt their behaviour and ours has caused us. It's usually having a limited understanding or perception of their behaviour that blocks us from loving them. When we realise that what was done to us was an extension of love, then we can learn to understand it. It was love, but not as we know it. If we learn love in a painful fashion when we are young, then we will only be able to give love as an adult in the same way. The person receiving this love will not be able to receive it and will find it unforgivable. We only remain unforgiving when we need to keep that person attached to us. Forgiveness allows the hold we have on that person to slip away. It leaves a space for a new feeling to come in along with reconciliation. We also have to learn that other people do not have to change for us to experience peace of mind. You can also let go of beating yourself up. When we have touched another person with forgiveness we no longer need anything from them. It is over and done with, it is complete. Forgiveness is understanding, it is not just pity. Forgiveness allows life to blossom and unfold.

4

energy healing
with colour

My father had the power to heal. He was a classic energy healer. A Scot, he was from a race who is said to be more naturally open to the psychic world than most. A long time after he died, my mother's cousin, Renee, confirmed a story from the time when he was lodging at my Granny Meyer's home.

My grandfather had extremely bad legs. They were covered in huge ulcers. For years, he had tried every kind of medical treatment. The doctors had given up.

One day my father said that he would heal Grandfather Meyer's legs. The family stood there amazed and silently wondered what my father thought *he* could do. He had only been in the house a few months and no one had noticed much evidence of his having any powers that would help his fellow man.

My father ordered a bowl of warm water, nothing else. After unravelling the bandages on Grandfather Meyer's legs, he scooped the clear water up in his hands and gently poured it over the infected ulcers. Then he wrapped them up again. The family stood there waiting, and thinking, 'Is that it?' Renee remembers her mother bending over to whisper in her ear, 'A fat lot of good that will do!' But within two days the ulcers had healed completely. Now everyone was truly amazed.

Regardless of the fact that he was a famous healer, I don't think my father ever realised the full depth and value of his gift of healing. It wasn't the kind of healer he had wanted to be. As a young man my father's ambition had been to be a doctor, but the Depression prevented him from going to medical school. I believe my father was a great healer. I've met very few people who could heal ulcers by bathing them in warm water. He had an uncanny knowledge of the human body; he seemed to know exactly how everything in it fitted together. When he handled someone's arms or legs, it was as though he could read them. He also had a great feeling for the state of balance of a person's body. He would often warn the person in whom he detected some disharmony that they would become sick or damage themselves unless they corrected it.

It gradually became known that John Grassom could heal where doctors had failed. People would often turn up on our doorstep from all over the country with just his first name: 'Is Jock the healer here?' pleading to be let into our house. He was wonderful with epileptics.

My father was very proud of his hands. He would hold them out in front of him and say, 'Look at these hands, they're beautiful, they're really healing hands.' It was true, they were exquisite. He was also a very melancholic person, but in a strange, backwards kind of way, his melancholia taught me the power of visualisation. 'Life is not a bed of roses,' my father would say. 'It is, it is,' I thought, 'I can see rose pink petals covering my bed, I can smell them.' Deep down inside me, I knew that life was magnificent.

The Advance of Colour Healing

The medical profession is becoming more aware of natural therapies for healing and looking at health holistically, so the colour therapist is not in competition with the medical world. Colour is an effective way of healing and complementing existing methods. But if you are on any medication or treatments, doctors would prefer you to check with them if you are in any doubt about a natural healing technique, and rightly so.

What are the best colours to use for certain conditions? I can give you information gleaned from my own experiences with colour. There are various ways of working with colour that help prevent many of life's mishaps, and that used alone or with other methods and treatments can speed up the healing process.

Colour as a healing therapy has come to many people's attention only in the last two decades. Yet it has a long and distinguished history as a means of healing. Colour healing was recognised for no less than a Nobel Prize for Medicine, received by the Danish physician Neils Finsen in 1903. He was awarded the prize for his work on light and colour in healing disease, the results of which were over 20,000 cures using both sunlight and artificial ultraviolet light. Other pioneering medical work on the healing aspects of colour was done by the physician Dr Dinshah P. Ghadiale in the early part of the 20th century. He did much to promote colour medically, healing with different coloured lights, a process he called Spectro-chromemetry – called *chromotherapy* today.

Disease has most often been treated as if it were nothing more than a malfunction of an organic machine – the physical body. But there are many interweaving and interlinked facets to the human organism, some of which are physical but others of which are purely energetic, and of which the physical body is a reflection. As we saw in the previous chapter, what we are often really missing is the connection to an essential part of ourselves, the part of us that exists as an integral part of the natural environment. The consequence of being not fully at one with that nature is illness, either physically or mentally. Colour is a powerful tool – it not only exposes that which is disharmonious but also helps to put it right.

It requires practice to develop the skills of using colour as a tool properly. But first, and above all we need to recognise that it *is* a tool, and that the skills to use it are available to all who make the effort.

Energy Healing

Colour healing both comes from and is an important part of the entire realm of energy healing. Colour is an intimate part of our being. The body acts as a prism in the light. When we are truly well, all the colours shine out from us in an ever-changing but always rhythmically serene lightshow. Then we become an ever-changing kaleidoscope of lights, the lights we truly are to one another. Auras, chakra balancing, colour-visualisation, food and drink, lighting and chromotherapy, as well as intuitive assessment, are all ways of engaging colour to heal on the energy level.

The Western world is finally beginning to accept that the human body is more than just flesh, that it has components that are energetic in nature, energies that are the manifest-ation of universal energies. Acupuncture, acupressure, reiki, and the laying on of hands, are all methods built on the recognition that the body's energetic nature is both reflected in and influences the functioning of the physical body, and that the body's energy flows can be influenced in a positive way through outside intervention. Colour is likewise one of these energies.

Colour is not only part of the environment, it is part of the very environment in which the human body evolved. Further, it is only within the narrow confines of the visible spectrum that our physical bodies can even survive. It comes as no surprise then, that our physical bodies have a very direct rel-ationship to colour. Understanding that relationship, and how to keep the body in a state of harmony and balance using colour – a state called *health* – has been the work of colour therapists and researchers for centuries.

Since the body has energetic components, the question naturally arises: 'What, exactly, is energy?' The answer is we don't know, and nor does science. Its properties as heat, as light, as atomic forces, can all be measured, but we can't say what it *is*. In a similar way, as we work with energy healing we can observe its effects; it works just fine without defining what 'it' is. A zone-therapist looks for the lines of energy flow within the body, called meridians, each of which has its own unique colour. These bands of colour have their own energy wavelengths, which is specifically why colour is used.

The Auric Field

Another way of seeing and understanding the body's energy flows is to observe the body's *aura*. Auras almost always appear to seers in various colours – colours which have

65

meaning, depending on where they are seen relative to the body. Books on the subject offer various interpretations of auric colours, but in the end most seers develop their own interpretations based on their own experience.

Most definitions of 'the aura' state that it is an energy field which surrounds the body of a person, animal, or even an inanimate object. This energy field emanates from within, and is extended out from the body or object. The aura encompasses energies at the physical, mental, emotional, and spiritual levels of being. It is made up of a number of layers, and it may extend outward two or three feet. Some see it as a shimmering mist around the exterior of the person, or as puffballs of coloured light escaping from the skin. It is also seen as shafts of white, dark or coloured light streaming outward from the body. Each of the chakras (see page 68) has its equivalent energy level represented in the aura.

A person's state of health can be determined by the purity of the emanating colours: vibrant, clear colours are a sign of health; dull, muddied colours indicate poor health. Disease can also show as black patches or spots, usually around the area where it is present in the physical body. Often the seer will have a strong intuitive sense of where disease is specifically located.

Emotional states are also reflected in auric colours. But unlike disease, these colours continually change as the emotional state changes. Reds and blacks in the aura are often associated with anger; greenish-brown often indicates jealously; and depression and fear frequently appear as grey.

More constant colours emanate from certain personalities: the proud and ambitious exhude orange; crimson flows from those with a passionate, loving nature; the intellectual radiates yellow; dark blue surrounds the very spiritual; light blue streams from those possessing noble ideals. Other personality traits also have their frequently seen permanent colours: dull brown from the avaricious; greyish green from the cunning and deceitful; greyish brown from the selfish. Clear green usually indicates a talented healer.

We all have a sensitivity to the emanations of others, whether we are conscious of it or not. No matter what outer face the person puts on, the aura reveals the inner truth of the person. Thus when we meet someone who we instinctively sense is not what they seem, we are, at least in part, reading their aura. Our auras always go before us and greet each other before we do so on the conscious plane.

According to the therapy practised and the indications given by observation of the aura, appropriate treatments, termed Energy Healing, can be given to the physical body, or, more often, to the energy body itself.

Seeing the Aura

Here is a simple exercise to help you begin consciously seeing auras. Start by looking just to the side of the head of the person. Let your eyes to go out of focus. The first thing most people see is a light grey or silver band an inch or two wide, surrounding the head. This relates to the electrical processes of the body. Once you can recognise this emanation you are already a seer, because even in this layer you can begin to get information about the person's state of health:

◆ Bright, light grey says the person is in generally good health.
◆ Black or slate grey indicates a depleted energy state. If you see this colour, introduce red by one of the methods discussed later in the book, such as visualisation, solarised water, or chakra energising, to boost the system.

◆ You may also sense disturbances in the area of one or more of the chakras: if so, boost the chakra energy using the method on page 71.

Your personal way of seeing auras will develop with practice. If you do not see colours at first, you will eventually. Many people will not see them visually, but will 'sense' them.

The Chakras

Another way of experiencing and working with the body's energetic nature for energy healing is through its *chakras*. Known as the coloured 'seven centres', chakras are spots of focus of various levels of energy at points along the spine, neck and head, spinning like a vortex. Each chakra has its own colour component, and a balance between them is necessary for good health.

These main chakras are positioned from the base of the spine up to the crown of the head. It is important to understand that chakras and energy focus are part of a larger understanding that the mind, body and spirit exist as part of the energy of the Earth and the Cosmos, and that disease is a reflection of disharmony at many levels – most of which are energetic.

Within the levels of energy that we embody exists a 'spectrum' of energies. At one end of the energy spectrum are the denser, purely physical energies that relate to the world of matter and reproduction, connected to red, and often described as 'dense', meaning they move at a slower pace. At the other end are the energies often described as 'spiritual': lighter, subtle, refined, easily overlooked in the hurly-burly of everyday life, and related to purple. Between these ends of the energy spectrum are five other levels, each relating to a different facet of life.

In general, red, orange and yellow are considered to be coarser energies, while blue, indigo, and purple are more ethereal. Between these, and neutral, is green. These levels each relate to an organ of the body, and each has a parallel colour which follows the spectrum.

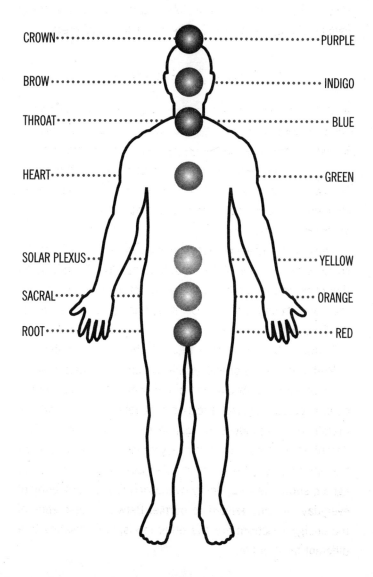

CROWN · PURPLE

BROW · INDIGO

THROAT · BLUE

HEART · GREEN

SOLAR PLEXUS · YELLOW

SACRAL · ORANGE

ROOT · RED

The location of the chakras is shown in the diagram on the previous page. The colours and their corresponding glands are shown below:

Chakra	Endocrine Gland	Colour
Root	Ovaries/Testes	Red
Sacral	Adrenals	Orange
Solar Plexus	Spleen	Yellow
Heart	Thymus	Green
Throat	Thyroid	Blue
Brow	Pituitary	Indigo
Crown	Pineal	Purple

The chakras likewise embody various human attributes. These can be strengthened or given emphasis by raising the energy of the associated chakra. These attributes are:

◆ Red Root Chakra: Sexuality, willpower, reproduction

◆ Orange Sacral Chakra: Assimilation, freedom, fearlessness

◆ Yellow Solar Plexus Chakra: Self-esteem, social identity, agility of mind

◆ Green Heart Chakra: Love, self-acceptance, relationships

◆ Blue Throat Chakra: Self-expression, patience, integrity

◆ Indigo Brow Chakra: Intuition, insight, structure, fortitude

◆ Purple Crown Chakra: Spiritual connection, humanitarian, mystic leader

Energising the Chakras

The chakras are often described as a rotating wheel or vortex of energy. In the following exercise you may find it helpful to visualise them as such. By applying the appropriate colour, their functioning is improved and balanced, giving an overall boost to the system or focusing healing on a specific area of the body. The method is simple:

◆ Close your eyes and visualise the colour corresponding to the chakra you wish to vitalise.
◆ With both hands over your eyes, visualise that colour flowing into the palm of your hands, and energising them with that colour.
◆ Place both hands over the chakra you are vitalising. Visualise the colour flowing into your body, directing the colour into to the chakra point.
◆ Repeat this procedure for any or all of the remaining chakras.
◆ Do each chakra three minutes at a time to align, restore, harmonise, and balance, as desired.

Colour Aids and Techniques

CHROMOTHERAPY: COLOUR PROJECTION

There is now a lot of research going on into the advantages of using colour, including investigations into ancient knowledge and how it can be brought up to date. Developed as a scientific therapy in modern times, the Ancient Egyptians, Babylonians and Assyrians have bequeathed us a legacy, as powerful today as it was then: chromotherapy. This therapy consists of bathing all or various parts of the body in coloured light. The application of coloured lights to the body can bring about enormous benefits. Every organ has its own colour vibration and when we are 'off colour' that vibration has become dull. The colours used in ancient times were the colours that the disease being treated caused in the body: yellow for jaundice, blue lips for a failing heart, fever-red for the skin.

The modern practice of chromotherapy is simple, and it is something that can easily be done at home, although best results are usually achieved from a qualified colour practitioner. In chromotherapy, coloured gels or slides are used with a light source. The need for either a pinpoint of colour or a wash of colour over the whole body determines the choice of the light source and its intensity. Through the use of high-powered adjustable lamps, which can be acquired from theatre supply shops, you can either bathe or pinpoint the body with whichever colour is required for healing. This can also be done using coloured light bulbs, or even with a coloured gel over a torch or flashlight. For whole-body bathing at home, coloured glass can be placed in front of a window; or if too expensive, cellophane can be used, although glass is better. A guide to which colour should be used for healing applications is shown on page 75, and in The Psychology of Colour chapter.

When working with chromotherapy, there are several general principles in its use that are important to keep in mind:

◆ The person being treated can either lie down or sit in a chair, with the lamp directed towards them. It's best they do not wear black or dark coloured clothes, and bright colours should also be avoided. A soft, neutral colour such as beige is best.
◆ If you use the prime colour only, exposure time should be limited to no more than ten minutes at any one session.

When using both prime and secondary colours in a treatment (see chart on page 75), allow five minutes for each colour.

◆ Treat conditions that affect the entire body, such as flu or colds, by flooding. Treat conditions affecting specific areas, such as a damaged knee or sprained elbow, by pinpointing, that is, by focusing the colour only on the affected area.

For use at home, certain colours have specific limits on their use:

◆ Red must never be applied to anyone with a heart condition.
◆ Never apply purple to the face; always apply it to the back of the head.
◆ Do not apply purple light to a child, as it is too strong.
◆ If a treatment is overdone, i.e. if the person has an agitated reaction and feels uncomfortable, flood with green light for a few minutes to neutralise, dilute and clear the previous application.
◆ Other cautions are listed under the information for the specific colours in Chapters 5 and 7.

The art of the colour therapist is first to diagnose by the use of colour and then find the unique treatment for that person. There is no format that applies to everybody. But with just a few simple implements and a knowledge of colour, this powerful therapy is literally a light bulb away.

Before going into other colours, let's look at white light. Many followers of colour seem to advocate it as though it were an antidote for all our ills. Agreed it does contain an equal measure of all the colours within it, but it can be too bright if used indiscriminately. Some therapists flood everything with it and then wonder why they have knocked everyone out. It can be too strong because of its powerful vibration. The white light should be confined to specific uses only. One of its most beneficial uses is for protection – you can surround your house with white light to protect it from vandalism and keep it safe. You could visualise a streak of white light surrounding a family member or friend who is travelling by car to keep them safe on their journey. White light will always protect you from any form of invasion. I refer to it as the 'clearer upper'. It can clear the air if there are bad feelings, or if something has left a nasty taste, such as the aftermath of a divorce. To clear the ground so that you can start afresh, just imagine a stream of white lava pouring from the top of a volcano, a beautiful, rich flow of light that will transform or destroy any ill feelings in its path. And when the ground has cooled after a flow of lava light, it leaves a richness of soil that is just perfect for rebuilding your life. Another way to heal with white light is to visualise a beautiful rainbow surrounding your body so that you are within a circle like an egg yolk. Visualise the seven colours gently floating around you in their bands and allow your body to take in the colours that you need for your well-being. Don't worry, your inner light will pull the necessary colours towards you.

White light is a potent force, never to be misused. Respect it as you would fire or electricity.

In chromotherapy, a qualified colour practitioner uses a principal colour, but introduces several other colours as well. For example, bedsores: as this is a skin complaint, the basic colour – the principal colour – for all skin conditions is yellow. Yellow will clear and strengthen the skin; by applying violet as a secondary colour, which consists of part red and part blue, the red will stimulate blood circulation drawing it towards the bedsore, and the blue will combat the pain. Always work with a bright principal colour. All dull shades need to be avoided when working for an alignment in the body.

The following table gives principal and secondary colours for a number of ailments. To simplify treatments, I have given just the principal colours plus turquoise.

TABLE OF PRINCIPAL AND SECONDARY COLOURS FOR CHROMOTHERAPY

A

Ailment	Prime	Second	Ailment	Prime	Second
Abcess	yellow		Alcoholism	indigo	green
Ache	indigo	lemon	Allergies	yellow	indigo
Achilles tendon	orange		Amnesia	purple	yellow
Acne	yellow		Anaemia	red	orange
Adenoids	indigo		Angina	green	blue
Adhesions	yellow		Anorexia	orange	yellow
Adrenals – overactive	blue		Arthritis	orange	indigo
			Asthma	orange	indigo
Adrenals – underactive	orange		Autism	orange	pink

B

Ailment	Prime	Second	Ailment	Prime	Second
Backache	indigo	green	Blood pressure (low)	red	
Bad breath	yellow	green			
Bedsore	yellow		Boils	yellow	red
Bingeing	green	pink	Bronchitis	indigo	orange
Bleeding	blue	indigo	Bruises	indigo	yellow
Blood pressure (high)	blue		Burns	indigo	green

C

Ailment	Prime	Second	Ailment	Prime	Second
Cancer	green	indigo	Constipation	yellow	orange
Cataract	indigo	purple	Coronary	green	orange
Catarrh	orange	yellow	Coughs	indigo	blue
Colds	green	blue	Cramp	red	indigo
Colitis	blue	green	Cuts	indigo	yellow
Conjunctivitis	indigo	purple	Cystitis	yellow	blue

D

Ailment	Prime	Second	Ailment	Prime	Second
Dandruff	purple	yellow	Diabetes	yellow	indigo
Deafness	yellow	blue	Diarrhoea	indigo	green
Dermatitis	yellow	indigo	Diverticulitis	indigo	yellow

E

Ailment	Prime	Second	Ailment	Prime	Second
Earache	yellow	indigo	Epilepsy	purple	indigo
Emphysema	indigo	orange	Eye problems	violet	blue

F

Ailment	Prime	Second	Ailment	Prime	Second
Fibroids	orange	indigo	Fibrositis	orange	green
Fever	blue	yellow	Flatulence	green	indigo

G

Ailment	Prime	Second	Ailment	Prime	Second
Gall bladder	yellow	indigo	Glaucoma	purple	blue
Gastritis	green	indigo	Goitre	blue	indigo
Gingivitis	blue	lemon	Gout	green	yellow
Glandular fever	indigo	blue			

H

Ailment	Prime	Second	Ailment	Prime	Second
Haemorrhoids	yellow	orange	Hepatitis	green	indigo
Hair loss	yellow	purple	Hernia	orange	indigo
Hay fever	indigo	green	Herpes – genital	indigo	yellow
Head colds	green	blue	Hodgkin's Disease	orange	green
Heart problems	green	gold	Hot flushes	indigo	orange

I

Ailment	Prime	Second	Ailment	Prime	Second
Impetigo	yellow	blue	Infertility	orange	red
Impotence	orange	gold	Influenza	blue	green
Incontinence	blue	indigo	Insomnia	indigo	purple
Indigestion	green	yellow	Itching	blue	yellow

J

Ailment	Prime	Second	Ailment	Prime	Second
Jaundice	green	yellow	Jaw pain	blue	green

K

Ailment	Prime	Second	Ailment	Prime	Second
Kidney disorders	orange	indigo	Knee problems	orange	gold

L

Ailment	Prime	Second	Ailment	Prime	Second
Laryngitis	blue	yellow	Liver disorders	green	indigo
Leukaemia	yellow	red	Lung disorders	indigo	yellow

M

Ailment	Prime	Second	Ailment	Prime	Second
Mastitis	indigo	green	Migraine	indigo	green
Menopause problems – F	orange	indigo	Mouth ulcers	indigo	blue
			Multiple Sclerosis	indigo	yellow
Menopause problems – M	gold	indigo	Mumps	violet	indigo
			M.E.	yellow	blue

N

Ailment	Prime	Second	Ailment	Prime	Second
Nappy rash	indigo	yellow	Nerve disorders	yellow	turquoise
Nasal catarrh	orange	indigo	Neuralgia	indigo	green
Nausea	green	blue	Numbness	orange	yellow
Nephritis	orange	indigo			

O

Ailment	Prime	Second	Ailment	Prime	Second
Obesity	red	orange	Osteo-arthritis	orange	indigo
Oedema	yellow	orange	Ovary problems	red	yellow

P

Ailment	Prime	Second	Ailment	Prime	Second
Pain – acute	indigo		Pharyngitis	indigo	blue
Pain – mild	blue		Pneumonia	indigo	orange
Palsy	yellow	red	Prostate – (to decrease flow)	indigo	
Pancreatic problems	yellow	green	Prostate - (to increase flow)	yellow	
Paralysis	red	yellow			

Q

Ailment	Prime	Second	Ailment	Prime	Second
Quinsy	indigo	purple			

R

Ailment	Prime	Second	Ailment	Prime	Second
Rapid heart	blue	green	Rheumatism	blue	red
Rashes	yellow	blue			

S

Ailment	Prime	Second	Ailment	Prime	Second
Sciatica	indigo	yellow	Sprains	orange	blue
Shingles	green	indigo	Stiff neck	yellow	indigo
Shock	orange	blue	Stress	blue	purple
Sinus	indigo	yellow	Sunstroke	blue	indigo

T

Ailment	Prime	Second	Ailment	Prime	Second
Thrush	green	blue	Toothache	indigo	blue
Thyroid (low)	orange	yellow	Travel sickness	green	blue
Tinnitus	yellow	blue	Tumours	indigo	purple
Tonsillitis	blue	indigo			

U

Ailment	Prime	Second	Ailment	Prime	Second
Ulcer	indigo	yellow	Urinary infection	indigo	blue

V

Ailment	Prime	Second	Ailment	Prime	Second
Varicose veins	indigo	orange	Vitality	red	orange
Vertigo	indigo	green	Vomiting	green	indigo

W

Ailment	Prime	Second	Ailment	Prime	Second
Warts	orange	yellow	Worms	yellow	indigo
Wisdom teeth	yellow	orange			

Complementary Colours in Healing

Every colour of the spectrum has an opposite colour that complements it. Complementary colours are particularly helpful in healing. They also find uses in everyday life: with them, you can pinpoint instantly the appropriate colour for help and relief. As an example, when you are extremely annoyed, and furious at someone's behaviour, you are reacting to an overload of the red energy within your system at that moment. Look at the colour wheel on the opposite page. Since the complementary colour to red (opposite on the colour wheel) is blue, visualise blue, wear blue clothing, or focus on a blue object. Do this until the anger passes. You might be in a room at a friend's house where yellow décor is unsettling. Close your eyes and visualise violet, yellow's complementary colour. It dispels the vibration of the yellow, and you can enjoy your stay.

Complementaries can also be of use when using chromotherapy treatment. Use a blue light to relieve the red of irritability. Or vice versa: use a red light to lift you out of the blues. Should you be in doubt about a colour or feel that you might have used too much of a colour, flood the person with green if using coloured light, or have them visualise it. Green brings back balance and order to any situation, acting as a neutraliser.

For the other complementaries, that of orange is indigo and the complementary of green is magenta, made up of red and blue.

In healing, the pastel colours, which have the most light in them will have the most power in them. Simply check how much light there is in it. Pale blue will have more healing power in it than dark blue. The principal colour would

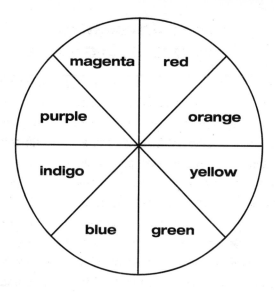

The Colour Wheel: The complementary colour is the one opposite each colour.

be blue, which, of course, is therapeutic in itself. Until full health is restored, leave the dark shade alone when aligning the body.

Hidden Colours in Healing

It is essential to be aware that when working with the turquoise colour for healing, the body will detect the vibration of the three hidden colours contained within it: yellow, blue and green. For instance, you may wish to use turquoise light on the body to treat a condition of the nervous system. You discover the person has high blood pressure. Because the yellow portion of turquoise is an expansive, stimulating colour, it will tend to raise the blood pressure even higher. In this case blue light is preferable to turquoise, as it is both soothing to the nerves and reduces the blood pressure as well.

Other Colour Healing Techniques and Tools

Aside from the techniques of chromotherapy, various other techniques and tools can also be used to promote colour healing.

◆ A torch or flashlight can be used to beam the appropriate colour onto an acupressure or acupuncture point while it is being stimulated.

◆ A jacuzzi bath can be illuminated with coloured underwater or overhead lighting. It is a wonderful and relaxing way of combining water with colour vibration.

◆ Coloured salt-rubs are helpful to invigorate paralysed limbs. They are made by filling a white linen bag with sea salt, and impregnating it with colour from a spotlight. Then, use the bag to massage gently over the area of paralysis; or, use them over the entire body for other complaints.

◆ Wrap different coloured silks around the body to envelop oneself in pure colour vibration. An indicator of its effectiveness is shown by the discovery several centuries ago that the scarring from smallpox was minimised by this technique.

◆ When sitting in a chair, nothing more than a small green silk square placed at the back of the head will relieve tension and pressure.

◆ Always refer to the Table of Principal and Secondary Colours on page 75 for guidance on the correct colours to use.

Colour Healing for Animals

Colour therapy is increasingly being used for animal healing. All animals with backbones have very sophisticated eyes, indicating their receptivity to colour. The energy structure of these animals is the same as in humans, and they have a large percentage of DNA in common with us. From my experience, when in need they respond well to the naturalness of colour for healing.

HEALING APPROACH

◆ Animals can sense your intentions and motives: they have highly developed perceptions and need to be treated with respect.

◆ Regard each animal as an individual.

◆ Let it get comfortable with you first. Gradually approach it.

◆ Let the animal come to you if it is walking.

◆ Speak softly and reassuringly. Do not rush – by your gentleness it will pick up your healing energy.

◆ Allow the animal to respond. It may be nothing more than a movement of the eye.

◆ Often an animal will draw attention itself to the affected area.

◆ Aim for ten-minute sessions once a week, or as many as seems necessary for a very sick animal.

◆ Animals know when they have had enough healing – they will either walk away or 'switch off'.

◆ The healer usually channels energy through the hands: place them either on the animal, or at a short distance away from it. The animal boosts its own natural healing through this in-flow of healing energy.

◆ Work on vertebrate animals along the spine, using the chakra colours as for a human – the tail end is the red, working up to purple at the head.

◆ A general colour for all animals when they are sick is orange. Use orange bedding for comfort and security, or a warm orange glow from a light bulb if this is not possible. After the initial crisis has passed, introduce tan, cream and green.

◆ Injuries initially need orange for a few days as this counteracts shock.

◆ Use indigo for tumours, blue for fevers, and red for malaise.

◆ Animals have a need for basic colour intake in their food just as much as humans. Although animal food is limited in its colour range, it is just as vitally necessary.

◆ Food should be light or even, and in small portions: brown is the best colour as it keeps the animal grounded and in their body. Introduce dark green through herbs and grasses during convalescence.

◆ Make clear drinking water easily available – the seven colours of the rainbow will be absorbed through the brilliance of water.

◆ Pets can be stressed by simple challenges such as the arrival of a guest, or even nothing more than loud noises. Relieve stress by introducing blue.

◆ After healing, use your hands to infuse the emerald green colour – or even wear green gloves.

◆ When an animal has reached the end of its life the inevitable needs be accepted – it's time for the greatest show of love you can give your dear, faithful friend. Purple, comprising blue and red, will quicken the transition in a state of peace and contentment. If the need arises for the animal to be put down let your love be a kindness to relieve physical suffering.

Colour and Crystals

In the past two decades we have experienced the growth of 'crystal consciousness', usually applied as crystal healing, yet their colours are the most neglected property of crystals. Crystals became prized originally specifically for their colours, especially transparent stones in intense colours – the first gemstones. Because the ancients had no means of separating out colours, they used naturally coloured materials. As noted earlier, colour healing was originally applied through the use of the same colour produced by the illness under treatment: yellow beryls were used for jaundice, bloodstone for haemorrhage, and lapis lazuli for the blue of restricted circulation. Diamond was prized for its brilliance, and considered a cure-all. A green copper carbonate, verdigris, was mixed with wax for the treatment of cataracts.

Colour is inbuilt into the very structure of crystals; it is one of the ways in which crystals perfectly balance their own internal energies. Thus for energy healing, coloured crystals are perfect. Much is written about 'crystal healing', and inevitably there is a list of illnesses and a list of crystals that are supposed to heal them. But what few have worked out is that a great many of these are the *colour* healing properties.

In an earlier section, auras were discussed. When crystals are brought into the aura, they interact with it, just like everything else. Because many of the inner dimensions that create the aura are intimately linked to colour, the use of crystals in combination with colour becomes a very powerful tool – a tool which creates understanding and inner harmony, called healing.

CHOOSING A CRYSTAL COLOUR

A common concern of those beginning to work with coloured crystals is of choosing the correct crystal. Simply put, there is no perfect stone for everyone. All crystals have their own worth and their own place in the healing equation. Resolve the dilemma when faced with a selection of stones by just picking up the one that most attracts you, often the first one your eye is drawn to. Or, just close your eyes and pick one up – your instincts will invariably be correct.

Here are a couple of other tips:

◆ Use your left hand if you are choosing a crystal for the purpose of touching into your intuitive physic ability. This is the side leading to divine power, directly through the heart.

◆ The right hand represents physical power and the ability to push troubles away. Use this hand for choosing your crystal colour if you want more mundane information relating to your day-to-day life.

The Laying On of a Crystal

◆ One useful technique for using coloured crystals is to lay the crystal on the body of the person receiving treatment, or it can be held just in front of or just behind the body.

◆ Have the person either lie down or sit in a chair.

◆ Place the coloured crystal at the afflicted place on their body, or hold it over the area.

◆ Visualise a stream of colour flowing into the area you are treating.

◆ For a general top-up, you can use a clear quartz crystal to lighten up the system.

◆ If you have only a general idea where the affliction is located in the body, place the crystal on or over the nearest chakra. If treating yourself, use the same procedure.

To choose appropriate colours, refer to Chapters 5 & 7.

'And life is colour and warmth and light
And a striving evermore for these.'
Julian Grenfell (1888–1915)

5

colour and parts of the body

Colour Yourself Well

As science has known for some time, everything in the universe is made up of a certain combination of vibrations. All organs and parts of our bodies, when healthy, hold to a particular set of harmonious vibrations or, in musical terms, notes. From this point of view, we can be seen as marvellously complex and individual pieces of music. If we become ill or diseased, it means that disharmony has crept into the music – off-colour means off-key. Even thoughts and ideas are vibrations and can be as 'unwell' as the liver or pancreas or any other part of the body.

Colours affect man totally. Man uses colour as an experience of feeling. Colour has the quality of zinging out towards you. It vibrates and hums until it sings to you, in the same way as music, except that colour sings to the eye and not the ear.

Colour healing is a wonderfully direct way of working upon the body. Neither flesh nor mental attitude nor emotion is a barrier to colour. Colour can go to the seat of a problem instantly. We can eat, drink, breathe, visualise, meditate and dance colour. We absorb more colour when we are unwell and we can apply colour to restore the bank of health.

In the following paragraphs you are given, under the related colour, the gland or other body part related to that colour, and specific directions about the use of that colour, and its shade or tint, where applicable.

brilliance

BRILLIANCE AND PARTS OF THE BODY

There is no specific gland related to brilliance, but brilliance is the aura of life's energy force, which reflects the inner light of a person. This luminous glow can be seen around the outside of a person's body by sensitives or psychics. It is the energy from which all colours emerge.

THE USE OF BRILLIANCE

We use brilliance when we want to bring about change, major or minor, in our lives. Brilliance allows us to wipe the slate clean. This shaft of pure light gives you a new page on which to write. The old blots go together with all tears and regrets. You can turn that page and move on in a new direction. The new direction can mean a change of house, career, partner, even country. Or instead of outer change, you may notice subtle shifts within you so that people say: 'I don't know you any more. You seem different.'

Healing makes use of the pure light. Many colour therapists consider brilliance a 'cure-all'. Brilliance has the power to modify any condition. Exposing the body to a spectrum bulb in a darkened room can begin the process of clearing things up, clearing allergies, chronic conditions – whatever affects you.

Florence Nightingale understood the value of light. Sunlight is a great antiseptic. When a room has no sunlight it becomes filled with bacteria and has a musty, putrid smell. The first thing she did upon entering any sickroom was to have the windows flung open to let the sunlight in. The Italians have a saying: 'Where the sun does not enter the doctor does.' You can do the same with any room that you feel needs cleaning: just visualise sending out a flash of brilliance to whip around the room.

I used brilliance techniques such as these to break through my reticence. That is, my fear of giving out what I see and know. By flooding myself with the clear light, I have been able to wash away all the fear and prejudice of using my psychic perception for other people that my childhood and social environment had instilled in me.

To clear and recharge yourself at any time, simply visualise a cascade of sparks of clear light pouring down through the top of your head and into your body and on out through your feet.

Jewellery gives us a constant reminder of the perfection of brilliance every time it sparkles and flashes light. Men and women have always adorned themselves with precious stones. Every time a flash of light sparkles from a jewel it reflects its owner's own relationship to that original light that is the essence of each of us.

Brilliance can be seen in a spark, in a burst of high thoughts, in a moment of ecstatic understanding, a tiny, tiny part of the brilliance that fills all levels and planes of consciousness with purity and justice. As a spark, I am part of the whole, hence the saying: 'There's a bright spark.' We are all sparks buzzing about, coming originally from the brilliance and the first point of light. A spark represents perfection and we are perfect just as we are.

Nature's way of helping us take in brilliance is in providing us with streams of pure, clear water. Water is liquid brilliance; bathing in a waterfall is the equivalent of standing under a cascade of pure light. Drinking clear water during fasting is a practical application of this cleansing aspect of brilliance.

Brilliance puts a crystal cloak over the earth as the dew every morning.

The clear message from brilliance is: 'In everything there is nothing, in nothing there is everything.' Brilliance's transparency can see right through.

◆ *Recommended exercise*:
The Ice Wall on page 251, uses the power of brilliance to clear away old blocks.

white

WHITE AND PARTS OF THE BODY

While each gland has a specific colour of its own (listed in each colour section), the collective functioning of the endocrine system is governed by white. White also represents the eyeball. The colour that is reflected from the eye white is used in diagnosing physical health.

White keeps the skin supple and moist. A masseuse in a Turkish bath in a tropical country noticed a marked difference in the quality of the skin of women who wore mainly white clothes. Their skin was softer and moister. The skin protected mainly by dark clothes was more wrinkled and pinched.

THE USE OF WHITE

White is primarily a carrier: it is host to every colour and favours none. When it is used for healing it needs to be combined with another colour or colours. The reason for this is that every part, organ and gland in the body has its own individual colour.

White, containing as it does equal amounts of all the colours, does not discriminate between one organ and another. This is an aspect of white's fairness and impartiality. White does not address itself to the particular colour need of a specific part of the body. Trying to heal with white alone is like eating a small amount of every known vegetable when what you really need is carrots.

It's good to wear white when the sky is cloudy. Our vitality drops on a dull, grey day. White can be used as a tonic to top up all the colours in our body's system. Wearing a white dressing gown is a simple way of swathing yourself in the healing white light. Use white to restore anything that has faded.

White can also be used in interior decoration, which is like giving your room an antiseptic wash. White sheds light in dark corners.

I sometimes use white with clients when they are having trouble opening up. If I see that a client is rigid or frozen, or has a one-track mind in some area, I will often use white so that they get a small amount of each colour. White helps them become less dense. It begins the process of cracking the ice; the blinkers begin to come off. White acts homeopathically and opens the person to the whole spectrum of colours.

◆ *Recommended exercise*: the *Star-Breath Technique* on page 117.

red

RED AND PARTS OF THE BODY

Red in the body refers primarily to the genitals and reproductive organs. The glands in the body connected to red are the gonads and the ovaries. Red also prompts the release of adrenaline into the blood stream when there is danger, aggression or pain – thus its connection to fighting or fear. The blood and circulation are a focus of red. Muscles, which give the power to act, are also a red concern, and red controls the body's temperature.

THE USE OF RED

Primitive peoples regard red as the life force. The lack of red blood cells of haemoglobin in blood causes anaemia. Anaemia emotionally signifies the loss of power somewhere in our lives so the blood becomes weak.

Another area of red focus is the genitals, the reproductive organs. Nature has used red to attract the opposite sex and ensure the continuation of the species by reproduction. Red is nature's sexual signal. We flush when sexually aroused; our lips go redder – which is why women wear lipstick! Sex has the power to enable two people to become one, albiet briefly, although nobody knows where we actually go at the moment of climax. Sex is a spiritual unity through physicality.

Irregularities in red show up as things clogging up in the circulation, or as irregularities in the blood supply, blood clots, furring up of the arteries, heart attacks, strokes, anaemia, and so on.

Red's polar opposites are growth and destruction. Neither is 'bad' nor 'good'. It depends on the situation and use. For instance, red's destructive quality could be used to destroy that which is holding up growth. One can see all illness as the attempt to destroy that which is holding up growth, including the body itself. Thus, death is part of the order of life's continuity.

Red is a good detoxifier. Red gets rid of rubbish from your life and psyche as well as from your body, and removes negativity. Magenta has a beneficial effect on the entire endocrine system.

The muscles, the power to act, are a red concern. Thus red will ease stiff muscles and joints. This is particularly true in the legs and feet, which come under the root chakra that red governs. Red is useful in cases of paralysis, particularly combined with physiotherapy. It stimulates. Red is good for anyone who catches colds or chills easily. The chill is the blue – fifth chakra, the throat – which the red warms. Red controls the body's thermostat. Use to counteract hypothermia.

◆ Remember, red can cauterise inflammatory conditions, but if used incorrectly it can irritate and aggravate all inflammatory conditions.

◆ If someone is stressed and irritated, avoid red.

Use red in a positive manner to focus your mind, and go with the flow of this colour. Red has thrust that drives you on to achieve greater things. So if you have something you are dreading doing, or are feeling low or sluggish in any way, just apply a little red for support and quickening. To do this, you can wear it, or put it about your house in the form of flowers, furnishings, decorations, red lighting, etc.

Just as red lifts, so too does it encourage shy people to come out of themselves. If you are somewhat backward in coming forward, add red to your wardrobe. It doesn't have to be much – like all strong colours, a little goes a long way. It is a good colour to start a business with, as it puts you in the hot seat. Red roots you. It brings your efforts to fruition.

CAUTIONS FOR THE USE OF RED

◆ Red aggravates all inflammatory conditions of both body and mind. If someone is stressed and irritable, red is to be avoided. (Remember the saying 'red rag to a bull'?)

◆ Red is a stimulant.

◆ Do not use red in a nursery.

◆ Professional colour advice should be taken for any heart problem.

◆ **DO NOT USE RED LIGHTING (CHROMOTHERAPY) ABOVE THE WAIST FOR HEART CONDITIONS.**

◆ **Recommended exercises:** for taking in red, or any tint or tone of red, the **Star-Breath Technique** on page 117; **Rainbow Tonic** on page 120 and **Water Solarisation** on page 131. *(Do not use dark red, maroon or russet red with these techniques. Because they have black in them, the red will be inhibited.)*

orange

ORANGE AND PARTS OF THE BODY

Orange is the area of the lower back and lower intestines, the abdomen and the kidneys. It governs the adrenal glands which are attached to the kidneys (although the actual colour related to the adrenal glands themselves is yellow).

THE USE OF ORANGE

If the orange is out of harmony, the next chakra above, the solar plexus (yellow), and the root chakra (red) below, will not be functioning fully. These three are the magnetic colours and are concerned with the action of earthing, making life happen for us in a real way, instead of just in our imagination. If their balance is dislocated, we will not be able to put into practice any course of action we may think or feel to do. Physically, orange links us to our intuition, which enables us to be masters of our own destiny. This feeling is gut instinct.

Orange is *the* colour for dealing with grief, bereavement and loss. When a person feels that they have been deeply outraged, 'It isn't fair', orange will bring them up through the shock. Orange can also reveal hidden shock and help us to expel it.

A person's dislike of, or resistance to, orange can indicate a fear of moving forward in life because they cannot bury the past. Orange can show that there is a hidden grief that cannot be faced. Often this shows up when a person has lost a loved one and feels that it wasn't fair. Orange is the colour to use to give strength to face and break such blocks. Orange pulls you through. Orange will always stir up dormant conditions. It provokes change.

Orange removes inhibitions and psychological paralysis. This fear of moving forward is related to the assimilation aspect of orange: the person has not been able to accept the past. The profound meaning of this is that *all* experiences, no matter how painful, have nutrients that we need. Orange helps us to absorb life's nutrients in the same way that our intestines draw off the nutrients in goodness from the food we eat. Refusing to take one's experiences into oneself stops the flow of the life processes. This is often the basis of anorexia. Orange helps increase the appetite.

Orange is connected to our gut instincts and feelings. When a person is working with the orange aspect within their system, they intuitively know what to do or what is right, regardless of the intellect.

Orange is useful for any intestinal disorders or bowel disturbances, also for kidney complaints. Orange also clears away any mucous or catarrh that may be in the system.

Orange can help in cases of mental breakdown, depression, rape, divorce and accidents. Autistic children respond to orange. It helps develop abilities that are blocked. Orange can bring in freedom from emotional paralysis.

Orange can aid with asthma and bronchitis, epilepsy and mental disorders, rheumatism, torn ligaments and broken bones. Orange binds together. It can be applied directly to limbs and muscles in physiotherapy.

Orange is useful during the menopause, particularly if combined with yellow. It is also an aid for infertility problems. It balances the hormones (for both sexes).

Orange can also reveal hidden phobias. It gives support to fight against unknown fears: 'I'm frightened all the time, but I don't know what I'm frightened *of*.'

◆ *Recommended exercises*: the *Star-Breath Technique* on page 117*; Rainbow Tonic*, on page 120 and *Water Solarisation* on page 131.

brown

BROWN AND PARTS OF THE BODY

Brown is not associated with any specific parts or organs in the body but nature makes us aware of its symbolic significance by our elimination process from the bowel.

THE USE OF BROWN

Being close to the earth, brown can give a cloak of security and earthy support during times of storm and stress. Brown is soothing; it allows us to snuggle up to the bosom of Mother Nature. Man is dependent on life that comes from the soil.

Wearing brown introduces the virtues of the colour into our system, as does having it in our home in any form of interior decoration.

People suffering from negative brown need to stand up and show their true colours once in a while. Cinderella is the perfect example of this. She had to leave the cinders and get to the ball to find her prince! Positive brown has the secret of renewal.

◆ **Recommended exercises**: the **Star-Breath Technique** on page 117.
◆ *A extremely therapeutic way of working with brown is to work in the garden, particularly turning the earth over and planting.*

yellow

YELLOW AND PARTS OF THE BODY

The yellow gland is the pancreas. Yellow is the solar plexus, the liver, gall bladder, spleen and middle stomach. The liver is known as the seat of anger, where all our emotional upsets and hurts are stored. Yellow is also the skin, nervous system and digestive system.

THE USE OF YELLOW

The solar plexus is the junction that absorbs all the emotions. Emotional upset will register here. Anything that adversely affects the solar plexus, or reveals itself by changes in that area, is likely to benefit from yellow.

Yellow's cleansing means healing. Yellow is the Great Eliminator. It cleans and removes waste from the system. On the physical level, it gets rid of toxins, and promotes the flow of gastric juices. Elimination is the law of life. Faulty elimination is the cause of the beginning of most disease. Yellow tones and cleanses the system. It relieves constipation. Constipation represents holding on to the past.

On the mental level, yellow clears out wooliness and negative thinking. On the emotional level, it clears out low self-esteem, the 'pardon me for living' syndrome.

Yellow moves things out. It purifies and increases the vital fluid in the body. Yellow is the great weight watcher. It balances the weight. Yellow, applied through chromatherapy or solarised water, is very good for removing cellulite.

Yellow stimulates the lymphatic system. It also helps with menopausal flushes, menstrual difficulties and hormone problems. Some people have found that it helps relieve the symptoms associated with diabetes, rheumatism and anorexia, and it clears the mind to help correct forgetfulness.

Yellow is also a brilliant colour to use with depressives. It is particularly useful for fears and phobias. Yellow clears congestion/catarrh. It is good for ear problems, skin rashes and abrasions.

Someone drawn to lemon yellow may be suffering from an acid system. The antidote could be best applied in a diet high in vegetables and salads, and low in grains, proteins and dairy *for a limited period*. Avoid acid-forming fruits such as grapefruit, oranges and plums.

Yellow is a very good colour in counselling. It tracks down deep-rooted reasons why your disease occurred. If I flood a client with yellow, it usually brings to the surface what the person needs to look at. It gets them talking.

Yellow helps transform 'I can't' into 'I can'. It also helps shyness and feelings of 'I'm not good enough'. Try using laughter therapy, the best yellow tonic there is. Laughter is internal aerobics; it massages your organs. Give your organs a treat. The best medication is a merry heart.

One of the best and most obvious ways of taking in yellow is to sit in the sunlight. Wear yellow clothing, sit in yellow lighting, introduce yellow flowers and interior decorations and furnishings into your surroundings to bring this, the brightest colour of the spectrum, into your life.

◆ **Recommended exercises**: the **Star-Breath Technique** on page 117; **Rainbow Tonic** on page 120 and **Water Solarisation** on page 131.

◆ A special technique for clearing the mind with yellow is given in the **Sun Shower Technique** on page 244.

gold

GOLD AND PARTS OF THE BODY

There are no specific body areas or organs connected to gold.

THE USE OF GOLD

Gold lifts you up. Thus, it is very beneficial for depressions, both physical and psychological. It is good for suicidal tendencies. It is also good for any kind of digestive irregularity, irritable bowel syndrome and nervous stomachs, and for rheumatics.

As yellow is useful for rashes and skin complaints, so gold, being stronger, is beneficial for scars. The best way of applying gold for this is through lighting – chromotherapy – and bathing the area in solarised water. (See **Water Solarisation**, page 131.)

Gold gives a feeling of well-being. It soothes the nerves. Gold means 'I am'. For this reason, it is good for depression during the menopause – which is based on a reluctance to let go of periods, and a feeling of being worthless as a female. However, in certain societies, a woman past menopause is revered. Freed biologically, she can now enter her most creative time of life.

Gold helps one to come to terms with what is. It also has a useful role during the male menopause.

A golden bandage for the wounded can be applied either materially or as a visualisation. Gold is extremely useful for the relief of past hurts, both emotional and physical.

One interesting aspect of gold is that it shakes off any kind of parasite – emotional as well as physical – anything that is not really part of you.

Introduce gold through wearing gold clothing and fabrics, jewellery, and through décor.

◆ **Recommended exercises**: the **Star-Breath Technique** on page 117; **Rainbow Tonic** on page 120 and **Water Solarisation** on page 131.

green

GREEN AND PARTS OF THE BODY

The green gland is the thymus. Green represents the heart, shoulders and chest and the lower lungs.

THE USE OF GREEN

Green is made of two primary colours: yellow and blue. Yellow is the last colour of the magnetic side of the spectrum, and blue the first of the electrical side. The yellow clarifies and the blue brings wisdom, so together as green, they help you remember all that you need to know. This is important because most of our physical and psychological illnesses result from events and conditions in our past. Green is also beneficial in cases of claustrophobia.

Green restores stability to anything malignant. Malignancy is the result of cells that have accelerated out of control. Green lowers this over-stimulation.

◆ *It is important to be aware that professional advice is necessary for the accurate dosage, and combination of, colours, for this kind of treatment.*

Recent tests in the USA led by Dr Paul Tacacy have found that eating broccoli fights cancer. It seems that a very potent compound, sulfoaphane, has been found in broccoli that behaves as an anti-carcinogen.

Green is best used as a bridge, a gateway to freedom. It can reveal the state of your heart emotionally, and physically, and your ability to relate. Green discriminates rightly. Unfortunately judgement and discrimination have become dirty words. But the truth is, without applying discrimination, we could not continue to exist. It's only when it becomes harsh and rigid that judgement does not serve us. After all, if you have two apples before you and one is good and one is bad, not using the green of judgement and discrimination before you select could mean that you end up with the bad one.

Green is the colour that blends with all. It is a general healer. If anyone is into an overload of any colour, just apply green to neutralise it.

An aversion to green often indicates that we don't feel happy with our emotions. Our conditioning as a child would have been: 'We don't want any of that emotional stuff, thank you'. It would have been stiff upper lip regardless.

Green helps dispel negative emotions. Green applied during stormy periods in a relationship will calm and cool the emotions. Green gives direction, so it can be used when you are trying to make up your mind or heart. It brings issues back into focus and is excellent for people who don't know what to do next.

Green is a tonic. For this reason, green is a good colour for therapists to use after seeing a lot of clients. If you're feeling scattered and frazzled, relax in a chair and put a green silk scarf behind your head; it will bring you back to the centre of yourself.

Green helps biliousness; soothes headaches. It is a good detoxifier and good for controlling blood pressure and liver complaints. It is also excellent for the treatment of shock and fatigue.

Green/gold is useful for nervous tics and stammering, and for anyone suffering from a severe neurosis. It heals the nerves. It brings the confidence of the gold and the calmness of the green to the person. Green/blue is a good aid for the physical heart, for angina for example. Jade/green is useful for manic depressives. Hold a piece of jade; use a jade coloured light, solarised water, etc.

Green is soporific. Green's calming qualities can be used with a hyperactive child. It gives reassurance, and so is particularly helpful with children coming from neglected and disturbed environments.

Green gives you a different view of a garden. From the coloured flower, which is our head, we go down the green stem of our body to the root cause of a problem. Green leads you to it – the diagnostic colour.

◆ *Recommended exercises*: the *Star-Breath Technique* on page 117; *Rainbow Tonic* on page 120 and *Water Solarisation* on page 131.

◆ A particularly good, easy and pleasurable way of absorbing green is through gardening, walking in the country under trees, or through the grass. House plants are a must!

turquoise

TURQUOISE AND PARTS OF THE BODY

Turquoise is connected to the throat and chest.

THE USE OF TURQUOISE

The healer for the emotions of the heart, turquoise can talk from the heart. It is the unity of the green and the blue (with yellow thrown in). When the green of the heart unites with the blue of the throat you can say what you feel instead of what is appropriate.

As it calms the nerves, turquoise is a great colour to wear if you have to appear before the public (especially when combined with a pink room, which makes the audience more receptive to what you have to say). It subdues. Turquoise is the slow but sure healer. It can sometimes take a while before you feel the benefit. Don't abandon using it for healing just because you don't get instant relief.

Turquoise feeds the central nervous system, so it is helpful in situations of nervous stress and breakdown. The stillness of turquoise calms the panic that can follow emotional shock. It stops the person running away from their hurt self, and the painful situation. A good colour to use when encountering problems in relationships, it encourages you to be able to speak what's in your heart. The inner resistance to turquoise that I sometimes encounter in clients is the fear of facing emotions.

Turquoise subdues fevers and cools inflammations of the nerves, so is particularly good for neuralgia. It is also good for skin rashes or inflammation, and for scar tissue.

Turquoise will be of benefit to anyone unable to decide between this side and that side of a question, or being aware of self-interests when making choices. It also encourages self-questioning; coming to know what one wants. It is useful in overcoming self-sabotage, and in centring oneself. If a person is drawn to this colour, you know they are getting down to the real issue of looking at themselves and how life affects them personally.

In American Indian mythology, the blue sky represents the masculine and the green of nature represents the feminine. When we wear turquoise we are uniting the sexes. The negative form of this shows coldness in relationships and lack of forgiveness.

It is important when using turquoise in any kind of therapy to remember that it is composed of three colours: blue, green and yellow. The practical effect of this is that the body will always be aware of the hidden yellow in the turquoise. Therefore, if you are going to use turquoise therapeutically, consult the yellow listing on page 97.

Turquoise may be introduced through clothing, jewellery, ornaments, fabrics and furnishings, décor, and lighting.

◆ *Recommended exercises*: the *Star-Breath Technique* on page 117; *Rainbow Tonic* on page 120 and *Water Solarisation* on page 131

blue

BLUE AND PARTS OF THE BODY
Blue's glandular domains are the thyroid and parathyroids. Blue depicts the throat area, and is linked to the upper lungs and arms, the base of the skull, and weight.

THE USE OF BLUE
Blue is the colour of the present time, the Aquarian Age. The Aquarian is the 'seeker of truth'. However, he or she must go

forward in truth. If they do not go forward, they will go backwards out of fear. Blue combats fear.

Because blue governs the throat, infections in this area are psychologically related to 'talking inwards', i.e., not speaking out. Psychologically speaking, coughing occurs because a person cannot trust themselves to speak out. Blue will help this by counteracting the fear of 'spitting it out'. People trapped in this negative blue syndrome need to learn the power of the spoken word – not so much to help others but to help themselves. They need to understand that what you don't ask for you rarely get.

Stiff necks can benefit from the application of blue. A neck becomes stiff because of rigidity of thought, a fear of going with the flow, of being flexible. Blue will help dissolve the fear.

Blue hates arguments. Rather than have a row, blue will refuse to say what it wants, will put up with the situation. People need *more* blue to get the courage to speak up. Bright blue is needed in such cases.

Blue is useful for children's ailments, and for teething and ear infections, also for childhood throat infections, and speech and vocal problems. Remember that your child may be unable to speak out from fear of the row that will follow! Also a child takes the energy of its parents' arguments. If the child is unable to say how upset it is, its throat tightens and becomes sore. The needy child is in the negative blue and needs to be encouraged to stand on its own two feet.

Blue can be used for the bedwetting child, and for adult incontinence. Add pink to blue for greater effectiveness The bedwetting child feels it is unlovable. Introducing pink with the blue counters this.

Blue in the sickroom cools and calms, and is particularly useful in reducing fevers, and for the terminally ill. Use a blue light bulb to flood the room with blue light.

Blue can make you aware of the need to rest and relax. Blue is *the* colour for modern-day stress and anxiety. Blue can help to bring down blood pressure. Introduce blue for relief of pain. Blue cools inflammation, helps nose bleeds, internal bleeding and varicose veins. It reduces the inflammational pain of sciatica and soothes stomach ulcers. Blue alleviates sunstroke.

A psychological use: blue counteracts harshness. If somebody is acting insensitively in a situation, blue may help them become more compassionate. Blue compensates: it can help a person realise the good to be found in a bad event or in a situation that cannot be reversed. Blue has an acceptance of that which cannot be changed. Blue gives relief from both physical and psychological pain, and combats cruelty and brutality.

Blue is not a good colour to wear if you want to lose weight. It is too static. I have observed that many people who are overweight feel an attraction to blue. This is because negative blue aids and abets them in remaining just as they are. Losing weight will bring confrontation, conflict and change.

◆ **Recommended exercises: the *Star-Breath Technique* on page 117; *Rainbow Tonic* on page 120 and *Water Solarisation* on page 131.**
◆ Surround yourself with blue in the home. Bring in blue flowers: bluebells, harebells, hyacinths, Canterbury bells. And most obvious of all, spend time under the blue sky!

indigo

INDIGO AND PARTS OF THE BODY

The indigo gland is the pituitary, sometimes known as the conductor of the orchestra, this being the endocrine system.

Physically, indigo represents the skeleton, particularly the backbone, lower brain, the eyes and sinuses.

THE USE OF INDIGO

Indigo is made up of dark blue and dark violet. The reliever of pain and fear, it is the one colour that shows up hidden fear – so if it appears in any process, look for a fear that you may not know you have. One strange aspect of this is that indigo can show a very deep fear of fire. This is very often related to an experience in a past life. Indigo is the colour that looks beyond the complaint itself and gets to the structural cause of the trouble.

Indigo is the strongest painkiller in the spectrum. It is an astral antiseptic that can clear up any bacteria, the results of air, water and food pollution, and astral toxins.

Because the area of the eyes and nose fall under its dominion, indigo is good for acute sinus problems and cataracts. Sinusitis and allied problems are uncried tears from childhood. Indigo is very good for lung and chest complaints such as bronchitis and asthma, and for the treatment of lumbago and sciatica, migraine, eczema, bruising and inflammation. Indigo helps to control diarrhoea. It is useful for bringing down high blood pressure. Indigo is the best antidote for insomnia that I know. I had a client who had not had a good night's sleep in 15 years so I suggested he use indigo with the *Star-Breath Technique*, on page 117. Two weeks later he told me he was getting a sound sleep every night.

Indigo is particularly effective for an overactive thyroid. It also helps with kidney complaints. Because of its particular relationship to the body's bones, indigo is beneficial in any kind of spinal complaint and backaches. Psychologically, backache means that we are holding ourselves back in life. Lower back problems relate emotionally to insecurity (usually money worries); mid back to emotional problems with relationships;

high back and shoulder blades to taking on too much – being put upon by circumstances. If you are drawn to indigo, it may be an indication that you need to look to the structure, i.e., the bones, of your life. Similarly, do this with addictions of any kind, such as drugs, cigarettes and alcohol.

Indigo is the great healer of painful memories. It is the great cleanser and purger, cleaning away addictive emotional ties. It helps a person to regain direction when they have been emotionally shattered. It helps prepare the way for the next step. Indigo helps you release yourself from imposed or self-acquired conditioning. Indigo will work if there is a real need. It is the power of mind and thought with understanding. It unravels the unknown.

Indigo disperses growths, tumours and lumps of any kind:

◆ *Visualise an army of indigo warriors moving through your bloodstream towards the tumour and breaking it up. Follow this with the visualisation of a green wash passing through the blood to the tumour site and flushing away the debris of the battlefield.*

Indigo is said to promote tissue growth, which is why it is good for burns:

◆ *Use an indigo bandage, flood the burn with indigo light, or drink indigo solarised water.*

To introduce indigo into your system, wear indigo clothes, jewellery; bathe in indigo light.

◆ *Recommended exercises*: the *Star-Breath Technique* on page 117; *Rainbow Tonic* on page 120 and *Water Solarisation* on page 131.
◆ Surround yourself with indigo in the home. And bring in indigo flowers: irises; pansies (pansy means 'eyes bright'); primulas.

purple

PURPLE AND PARTS OF THE BODY

The purple gland is the pineal. Physically, purple represents the top of the head, the crown, the brain and the scalp.

THE USE OF PURPLE

Purple is to be used sparingly. It is a 'heavy' colour, and too long an exposure to purple can be depressing, and even bring out suicidal tendencies. Purple can find itself going round and round in circles to find an answer. When there is no solution, it can decide to depart – in more ways than one. Purple can be beneficial to calm people who are emotionally erratic.

Purple can bring about its own form of isolation. If you have ever felt lonely, or apart from life, just acknowledge your own individuality. Leaders are always men apart – and be assured that it is all right to march to the beat of a different drum.

Purple is good for subduing palpitations of the heart, and is a helpful colour for head, scalp and concussion problems, jangled nerves and the immune system. Purple is useful for any kind of *internal* inflammation. It is also useful to help skin eruptions subside.

One very positive way of using purple is let it help you bring your leadership qualities to the fore.

Purple helps with the pain of neuralgia and acute inflammation of the nerves. Can be used for eye complaints – breathing techniques are safe enough for this. It is linked to the unborn child, thus its use with infertility problems. It is also good when working with one's own inner child for this lifetime and can be used in regression work to heal yourself when a childhood arises from a past life.

◆ *The direct application of violet light should only be done under the supervision of a chromotherapist.*

Lavender is the colour of convalescence, and also the colour to use to clear anaesthetics from your system. Because lavender works on the brain's pain centres it helps with drug addiction. (Drug addiction is suicide of the soul.)

Lilac generally has great healing powers: it strengthens the immune system.

CAUTIONS FOR THE USE OF PURPLE

◆ *Purple is not a colour recommended for use with children.*
◆ *If it is used with children, exposure times should be very short.*
◆ *Purple light should never be directed onto the face, but applied only to the back of the head.*
◆ *Should anyone have an overload of purple, the antidote is exposure to gold – gold lighting, décor, clothes, etc..*

To introduce purple into your system use purple clothes, ornaments, jewellery, coverings, flowers, etc. Violet and lilac flowers include stocks, delphiniums, irises, and of course violets and lilac.

◆ ***Recommended exercises:*** the ***Star-Breath Technique*** on page 117; ***Rainbow Tonic*** on page 120 and ***Water Solarisation*** on page 131.

grey

GREY AND PARTS OF THE BODY
There are no specific body areas or organs connected to grey.

THE USE OF GREY

The positive of grey is that it is useful for diagnosis. Grey's ability to show up blemishes and spots in the body is used in X-rays. Grey is not a colour that is used for healing specifically. Rather, it can predict illness – it gives information on the state of the person, mentally, emotionally and physically.

Grey is the light that is dimmed. It shows a fear of circumstances that calls for colours. People who wear grey suits are armouring themselves against the negative aspects of grey – illness, criticism, fear and restriction. When life is grey and bleak, it is colourless and flat.

However, grey can free from the chains that bind. It provides an alternative. A bleak view of the future can be turned around by grey. It gives the inner strength necessary to face up to and begin changing a hopeless situation.

Black-and-white décor in a house often shows that the owner/s may be approaching the grey state that says: 'I want to leave.'

If the whites of the eyes are grey, or if the fingernails, the skin or the urine has a greyish tint, it shows a thickening of phlegm or catarrh in the nose, chest, stomach or bowels. The antidote is orange.

Grey restores sanity and it stops self-deception. It can also be used profitably with someone who is utterly reckless and irresponsible. It can sober up such a person. Grey is a great colour to subdue the nerves when shattered.

Grey can be worn or used in décor around the house. A particularly good, easy and pleasurable way of absorbing grey is to take a walk under a grey sky. A soothing silver-grey is beneficial in aiding sleep.

silver

SILVER AND PARTS OF THE BODY

There are no specific body areas or organs connected to silver.

THE USE OF SILVER

Silver reflects back mistakes without distortion, apology or bias. A mistake is not necessarily negative. We learn from our mistakes. A mistake is growth. It's only a mis-take after all – like filming, you just do it again until you get it right. This ability to mirror is very useful in therapy. A mirror never lies ('Mirror, mirror, on the wall...').

Silver is very good for calming the nerves. The spiritual tranquillity and harmony associated with silver bring about a fluid state of consciousness. Silver calms the hormones. Silver is good for the functioning of the kidneys, and beneficial in the fluid flows in the body.

To restore equilibrium you can introduce silver through jewellery, wearing silver clothes (evening gowns and suits), carrying a silver handbag, silver shoes and accessories. A very good way of absorbing silver is to fling your curtains back and bathe in the moonlight. Star-gazing is a therapeutic silver pastime, also. Making love in the moonlight is said to be a magical and mystical experience!

◆ *Recommended exercise*: the **Star-Breath Technique** on page 117.

black

BLACK AND PARTS OF THE BODY

There are no specific body areas or organs connected to black, but black spots in the aura indicate disease. If black is seen in the aura, it means illness or a darkness of the soul.

THE USE OF BLACK

The basis of the positive use of black lies in the paradox that in the heart of black there is light. A simple indication of this is something that we experience every night: we are asleep in a dark room and dreaming, but where does the light in our dream come from? This light in the heart of darkness is the secret of black. One everyday expression of our understanding of this is: 'the light at the end of the tunnel'. This is an ancient teaching about the mystery of light and dark. The Bible, in the first paragraph of Genesis, says about the mystery of the Creation: 'God saw that the light was good, and he separated light from darkness. He called the light day, and the darkness night. So evening came, and the morning came, the first day.'

Our problem with black is in not going far enough into it to discover the light. No colour is either 'good' or 'bad'. Even the negative aspects of black can be used positively. Sometimes we need to destroy the old and habitual to clear the way for the new to come in. We can overcome the fear that as the sun sets, it sinks not to rise again.

Black, for all its holding, constrictive qualities, can also be wonderfully liberating. Of course, there are right and wrong ways of going about destroying the old. Black more than any other colour shows up one's vices and virtues. Darkness always indicates a loss of energy which only comes when there is weakness or congestion. Just bathe in the white light to clear it, followed by orange.

Someone wearing black continuously may be saying that there is something absent, something lacking, from their life. If someone is held back by circumstances that they are fearful of breaking free from, black may become the colour they feel most comfortable in. Why? Because in black they do not have to move on. It is what they cannot face that keeps a person in the black. Black in this case is like the womb; a safe and hidden place in the world.

However, too much black will keep a person from discovering what is missing, or it will keep them caught in the circumstance. It would be better for the person to get out of black and into colour. Knowing what other colour to introduce is where the art of applying colours to your life lies. It is not as difficult as it might seem at first glance. Your own common sense plus the colour information that you have already read in this section will be enough to begin experimenting.

People taking refuge in black are in a state of depression. Life's disappointments have sent them into the *negative* of black, having lost the promise of growth that the *positive* of black gives us. They have decided it is time to retreat. They want to 'black out' for awhile. Black is their personal 'no man's land'.

To break the hold of negative black, colours must be introduced. This will begin to bring some movement into the person's static state. Black combined with another colour can show the outcome. Red and black will make up for all that is deficient. Yellow and black shows a happening will put it right. Blue and black shows that the person is only prepared to enter life in a calm and tranquil way.

Black also completes the incomplete. Nowhere is this seen more clearly than when we use the black of sleep to complete our life's unfinished business in our dreams. Black gives access to the material of our lives.

Another aspect of the light in the heart of black is discipline and freedom. Black is discipline, it has a restrictive quality. It brings order out of chaos. You can use the restriction and discipline of black to gain true freedom. You do not have to go to sleep to use black in this way. Meditation and visualisation are a way of dreaming while awake. For instance, a therapist could use black at the right time to help an addicted patient look at the original cause of his addiction by putting him in a dark room and leading him through a visualisation. The dark room will envelop the person and keep him or her on hold long enough to break through and see the light, i.e., the cause of the addiction.

Remember with black that it will always encourage you to work from what you know rather than from what you see.

The age of the person who chooses black must be considered when its significance is being interpreted.

◆ *Teens:*

Teenagers wearing their black leather gear are announcing that they are ready to take control and run the world. They are not going to let their parents or society tell them what to do any more. They believe they can make a better world than their predecessors. 'Freedom' is their cry and breaking chains their aim.

◆ *20s & 30s:*

Black worn obsessively in the 20s and 30s indicates that the person's life is on hold. Something has brought it to a halt. The person is boxed in.

◆ *40s:*

By the 40s we should be at ease with power. How we relate to black at this age shows how we have come to terms – or otherwise – with power and control. A strong attachment to black at this age indicates those issues are yet unresolved.

◆ *Recommended exercise*: the **Star-Breath Technique** on page 117.

pearl

PEARL AND PARTS OF THE BODY

Gallstones are made of the same substance as pearls, a mineral called aragonite.

THE USE OF PEARL

Gallstones are a gift to us if we understand their meaning, which is that our emotional life has been disturbed. As children we are usually emotionally vulnerable. It takes experience to learn to be quick enough to protect ourselves from invasion (in the way a grain of sand invades an oyster to create a pearl).

Pearl aids digestion by promoting a dislike for fatty foods, so it is a good colour for the overweight person. Pearl is also a general healer for the body's subtle energies. An aversion to pearls could indicate problems with the gall bladder. Spasms and cramps are related to the pearl aspect.

The best way to introduce pearl is to wear it. It can also be absorbed through mother-of-pearl accessories, décor and furnishings. A pearl food is oysters.

◆ *Recommended exercise:* the **Star Breath Technique** on page 117.
◆ Pearl can also be 'drunk' if a real or cultured pearl is left overnight in a glass of pure water.

◆ One of the best ways of taking in pearl for therapeutic purposes is through bathing in the sea. (Seaweed baths are a good substitute.)
◆ Another way is to have a clear glass full of pearl beads (without water) in a room, or standing beside the bed.

Exercises

THE STAR-BREATH TECHNIQUE

With this technique you can relieve pain with three breaths. Wherever you are, you can breathe in the colour antidote.

Before you begin the actual process, you need to work out which colour will best counteract the particular emotional, physical or mental state you are suffering from. Use this chapter or The Psychology of Colour chapter for guidance. Or just go with your intuitive feeling for the colour you need.

This is a visualisation process. Don't worry about visualising – if you are able to imagine, then you can visualise. To prove you can imagine, just think of a time when you were happy. Picture the scene, whether it was a party, a wedding, or whatever. A mental picture will come into your mind, and that is visualisation.

1 First, sit comfortably and relax. It is better to sit up with your spine straight – if you lie down you may go to sleep! (To prevent this, if you do lie down, just keep one arm raised in the air, so if you do fall asleep your arm will drop and wake you up.) Now that you are relaxed, you can concentrate on your colour visualisation. Clear your lungs by taking three deep breaths, inhaling strongly, exhaling slowly.
2 Visualise an indigo sky full of silver stars ...
3 Choose one of the stars as your star – one of them *does*

belong to you. Once you have found your star, you will use it every time you carry out the Star-Breath process.

4 Choose the colour that you need for your healing.

5 Switch your star on so that it beams down a ray of the colour you have chosen. This ray should be broad and powerful. See it filling the air around you with its colour radiation.

6 Breathe in for the count of three, visualising yourself inhaling the colour as you do. Visualise this strongly. Actually see yourself pulling the colour out of the air in through your nose and watch it flowing into your body.

7 Hold your colour-breath for the count of three.

8 Exhale for the count of three.

9 Repeat stages 6, 7 and 8 two more times. This completes the three in-breath, out-breath colour cycles.

It is important to take the in-breath in through the nostrils. Exhale through the nose – unless the pain or condition is acute, when the out-breath should be through the mouth. This applies particularly for severe pain or any kind of shock.

You can use the colour-breath to fill the whole body, or if you are attempting to remove a particular pain, direct the colour-breath to whatever organ or part of your body is in pain. If the first three breaths do not achieve the result you want, continue the process for two more three-breath sets. Once you have established your colour-breath star, you will find that you can turn it off and on at will.

The Star-Breath process is invaluable for situations where other help is not immediately available.

◆ The Star-Breath is also a good process for childbirth, using a different colour for the three stages of labour. These vary depending upon the delivery.

- It can be used in many ways throughout pregnancy. For morning sickness, for example, try having your star beam jade green or lemon.
- It is also a very useful technique for calming the nerves before going on stage, before an interview, or for any situation that is unusual or creates stress. Try turquoise for this.
- On the other hand, someone who needs to be energised to meet the demands of an important business meeting where they will need facts and figures at their fingertips could try breathing one set of three green breaths for memory, and one set of three scarlet breaths for impetus.
- Children take to this process easily. Orange and peach, for instance, will help a child regain his or her lost appetite after illness.

If you find that the colour fades after a few breaths, it means your body has absorbed all it needs of that colour and has automatically shut off.

A Night Variation

Visualise your star in the indigo sky just before you go to sleep. Turn it on and allow the colour to beam down on you. You will be inhaling it as you sleep. Your star will fade away without your conscious control when you have had enough. Once again, have the star beam to you whatever colour you wish to work with.

- Indigo is a good choice for insomnia.
- Indigo is also a good choice for acute pain. It is the strongest colour to relieve pain. This is a wonderful technique to use for people in hospitals or hospices to control pain.
- If you're lonely or restless, a warm pink will be comforting.

Just flood yourself with pink and away you go into dreamland, warm and secure.

◆ If you have a trying day ahead, involving facts and figures, leaf green helps prepare your mind for this kind of work.

◆ Once again, to choose the best colour, work with both the information in Chapters 5 and 7, and your own intuition.

◆ It is probably best to avoid the bright magnetic colours – red, orange, yellow – for night-time use. Tints of these colours such as pink, peach or primrose would be safer.

Whether using this process awake or asleep, use only one colour at a time for each set of three breaths.

Rainbow Tonic

This is a wonderful way of topping yourself up with one or more colours. It is something you can do on a regular basis just as you might jog two or three times a week. It comes under the heading of taking care of yourself.

A good time to use this exercise is whenever you have to wait somewhere, or when you are travelling home from work in the evening, or on a long plane or train journey.

Among other beneficial effects, the regular use of the Rainbow Tonic exercise helps you to be receptive to colour. It actually raises your colour absorption level.

1 Make yourself comfortable in a chair. Close your eyes and relax. Focus on your breathing by taking in deep breaths and exhaling slowly.

2 Visualise a sky of pale blue. Across the sky stretches the arc of a rainbow.

3 Focus on the red band of the rainbow. The red band now starts to vibrate. Be conscious that the red vibration is now leaving that band and coming towards you like a rich, red cloud. As the colour nears you, it disintegrates into a million fine ruby crystals. These shower all over you!

4 As the crystals touch your skin, they become very fine ruby-red droplets of water. This water sinks through your skin and into your body. Your body fills with this colour, being gently warmed, rejuvenated and regenerated.

5 When your body has absorbed enough of the red vibration, the pores of the skin will gently open and the excess will escape as a red mist that swirls softly around your body, gently touching your face and skin lightly. Within a few minutes, the mist will evaporate.

6 Repeat this process with the next colour band in the rainbow, which is orange.

7 Continue until you have absorbed all seven colours of the spectrum: red, orange, yellow, green, blue, indigo and violet.

◆ It is perfectly all right to use just one or more colours rather than the whole seven. However, if you do this, make sure that you use the magnetic colour or colours (red, orange, yellow) before the electrical (blue, indigo, violet).

◆ Another point: this process can be used for colours that do not appear in the rainbow, such as turquoise, gold, lemon yellow, jade, etc.

◆ One thing to notice is the difference in your absorption times for different colours. If one takes longer than most, check the positive aspects in this chapter or The Psychology of Colour chapter to see what you were replenishing.

6

the colours we eat and drink

Why Life is Not Just a Bowl of Black-and-White Cherries

Colour is, I believe, an essential food. There is such a thing as colour starvation. Colour is as necessary to us as food is for our stomach, or air for our lungs. Getting the balance right is a major *preventive* of disease.

There was a report in *The Times* (London, August 1991) about some of the hostages in the Lebanon who, on their return, were given a bowl of red cherries. They had not seen colour for three years and they just sat and 'looked at the cherries for a whole day in spite of an overwhelming desire to eat them'. The report said that they could not take their eyes off the red.

Red is the colour that connects us to life and life's energy force. It directly affects the blood and the circulation. It gives us zest, moves us forward. It gives great courage, and it is expansive. These were just the qualities that the men most needed after three years imprisoned in a small room. They had been literally starved of the red vibration. They needed to soak up the colour of the cherries more than they needed to eat the flesh.

Furthermore, colour tells our body what kind of nutrients a specific food contains. The nutrients are colour-coded. One day we will find ourselves drawn towards red foods, another day green. The colour vibration tells us which food has the nutrient we need.

Understanding the connections between colour and food offers a key to remaining healthy. We are all sensitive to the colour of food. Our appetite will be increased or decreased by its colour. Why are foods coloured anyway? Why aren't they all just black and white like old movies? The answer is because there is an essential connection between the vibration rate that is a particular colour and the pattern of nutrients a particular food provides.

Different coloured foods are a good way of putting the colours we need into the body to improve and maintain health. Each food has its own vibrational rate. Red foods fuel and charge the body; they fortify the blood. Yellow foods are the natural laxatives, and citrus fruits, the colours orange and yellow, are the stimulators and eliminators. They are the most highly vibratory coloured foods we have. Orange juice first thing in the morning can help to remove undigested food left over in the system from the day before. Green foods cleanse the system. Green herbs represent the bloodstream or the circulation of the plant kingdom. The bright green chlorophyll that comes to us in green plant life is the greatest rejuvenator you can put into your body. Green is the sunshine vegetable. Green food is loaded with sunshine – that's why it's green.

Even if a person doesn't like vegetables or salads they have to admit that the food looks appetising. The added bonus of green is that it puts you off white sugar. We can get natural sweetness from vegetables and fruit.

Food is another way of introducing sunlight into the body. The natural juices of the fruits and vegetables we eat are the plant equivalent to blood in the human system. But they must be fresh. If food is picked before it is ripened to its full time, it is robbed of sunlight and will not develop the full range of minerals and vitamins.

Light is a nutrient and like food is necessary to health. Foods eaten that grow above the ground carry imprisoned sunlight – they are sun-charged. Vitamin D is derived from sunlight, so when we sunbathe we are sun-charging our bodies. It is advisable to eat three parts of vegetables grown above the ground to one part grown below for the maximum health benefits.

Some foods can be disharmonious with our metabolism, in which case they are likely to cause imbalances in the body. Watch out especially for junk foods that have been chemically treated or processed in some way.

Furthermore, our emotional state can turn food into this kind of unbalancing energy. If we are angry or upset, the vibrational rate of the food we eat is upset. Food should be eaten in an atmosphere of calm and harmony. We need to be aware that there are calming foods and stimulating foods and foodless foods. Overcooking food can also cause the vibrational rate to be changed. We can kill the vital colour.

Foods exposed to different coloured lights will also be affected. Red light seems to lighten heavy bread – it seems to expand it. Any food or water that is passed under the sun seems to be lighter (enlightened?) and has a marked quality about it.

We must be aware that we can create different colour combinations with the food we put on our plates, so if we have green, blue and yellow foods, for instance, they combine to make the colour turquoise and we will receive the vibratory action of that colour. Likewise, red and yellow foods will produce orange vibrations.

If there is an overload of any particular food, you can always balance it by using its complementary colour.

Depending on the choice of foods you make, you can build disease or health. Understanding this could give you the answer to various ailments, the commonest being indigestion – after all we cannot have sweet thoughts with a sour stomach. All our bodily functions will try to maintain us in a state of well-being. As long as the law of nature is in force, which is an input of decent colour co-ordinated food, we will remain in perfect harmony. In short, be aware when cooking that you create a meal in which you have combined the colours for balance. A plate of food that is all one colour is not balanced.

If a certain colour is missing from the food itself, supply it by the table decorations, the flowers or the napkins. Then at least the colour can be taken in by the eye if not by the mouth.

So, understanding the connection between colour and food offers a key to remaining healthy. We are all sensitive to the colour of food. For instance, we will always be stimulated by red foods – they will make us eat a lot. White and brown foods are found to be the most popular coloured foods eaten in restaurants. This is because the brown represents the goodness of the earth and white represents mother's milk – nurturing. Being drawn to white is putting us in touch with our emotional connections to security while being nursed as a child. I personally feel that we don't need milk like other animals; I can see no reason for humans to have milk once we are adults. We are definitely not drawn to food that is blue, perhaps it is because we get the blue vibrations from the sky.

But, as so often happens with us human beings, there is a complication. We can also be attracted towards foods that we definitely do not need. These foods, while trying to restore a balance to the system, actually create a further imbalance. Why, for instance, should a person find himself or herself eating chocolate at every possible opportunity? Consider it from the point of view of colour, consider the colour brown.

Brown is the colour of a person who is inhibited, who does not want to be all that they are, who wants to hide their light under a bushel for some reason. Being attracted to brown often indicates someone who is insecure, and frightened to expand to their full potential. Such a person lives their life like a little seed in its brown husk in the ground, afraid to take in the life-nutrients around it which would cause it to explode into growth, rise up through the ground and into the air to bloom.

One of the well-known side effects of chocolate is that it makes a person fat. Being fat is an excellent way to be unattractive in a society that worships slimmers. Being unattractive is a way of avoiding our sexuality because we are frightened of it. In other words, the brown chocolate helps the person keep buried their power to attract others. Why they are afraid of being attractive, and where and when they learnt that fear, is something that colours can also reveal. Fat is fear. Continual fear causes a person to be fat and weak. There is a lack of firmness in the person's life.

Another reason why we may over-indulge on chocolate is because somewhere in our lives we are not getting our own way. Eating chocolate is getting your own way – it may be the only time in your life where you can fulfil your own needs. 'I need chocolate. I'll have it. I can't get what I want anywhere else in my life, but this way I will get my needs met.' That's why it's so hard to give up chocolate or any other food that substitutes as a nurturer. Bingeing literally fills a gap. The problem is the food can never be enough because it isn't appropriate for the food to fill an emotional need. It has been proved that 97 per cent of people on a diet today will be on a diet next year, and some will be even more overweight!

This is not to say that a fat person consciously does not want to lose weight. They often do, desperately. But the person who is imbalanced – which simply means unable to be his or her real self – will often choose the foods or colours that will tend to keep them in a state of imbalance. Those who crave white chocolate are likely to be expressing the extreme frustration that white denotes. White represents our mother's milk which gives sustenance, so when our addiction is to white chocolate we are saying that our feeding times as a baby were not satisfactory. We do not blame our parent for this, she did her best. It's just how our inner child perceived it. Unfortunately, if the mother for some reason is under undue pressure she may become hostile to parenthood. Her mother's milk for her baby will then be 'poisoned'. This can lead to eating disorders in the child. Distrust sets in which leads to the non-absorption of food syndrome, anorexia, and to food allergies. The same is true of those of us who overeat, as it is of addictions or eating disorders of any kind. In overeating or bulimia – a bingeing and purging illness which is a self-hatred syndrome – the colour of the food the person overeats will often give a clue to the deeper problem.

Another addiction is caused by brown alcohol. Brown makes you want to shrink away, to hide or go to sleep – which is just the way you feel the morning after a drinking session. As brown comes from a mixture of the warmer colours, use the opposite end of the spectrum, the cooler blues or green the great neutraliser, to conquer the effects of alcohol.

I find it interesting to notice the colours of the foods people choose when I am out to dinner. If you have a knowledge of the psychology of colour, you can always see where a person is by the colour of the foods they choose. For instance, if you are having a business lunch and you are considering giving your guest a job, and you need a quiet, reliable and un-assuming person for the role, if they assure you they are of a retiring disposition and then they choose a lot of red, forget it! They'll no more stay in the background than fly to the moon. Brown or indigo food, however, would be entirely another matter. (You can find a list of coloured foods and drinks on page 144.)

Understanding the connection between colour and food offers a key to remaining healthy. We are all sensitive to the colour of food. When the Indians in Peru found that they had fallen out of balance, which is another way of saying 'fallen ill', they would put themselves in a state of great receptivity and then go out and walk quietly through nature. It is said that, in this state, they were able to hear the herbs or grasses or leaves that they needed to correct the illness speak to them. It's a lovely story, and it is more than just a story.

We have the same abilities. The same intuition, which simply means 'in-knowing' or 'in-teaching', lives within us. But we have lost our connection with it. For a long time, its value and truth, even its existence, have been denied in our society. I am sure that our health and well-being, both as individuals and as a society, depend upon our recovering that lost connection so that we can once again hear what nature is saying to us.

Quite often, though, we go in exactly the opposite direc-tion: we drown out the inner voice and steer 180 degrees away from what we need to restore our well-being. We can be so imbalanced in ourselves, physically, mentally and emotionally, that we are unable to recognise the foods and the colours in life that would help us recover that lost balance. We have forgotten that it is wiser to eat first what we need and then, if we must, eat what we would like.

Our body will actually be drawn towards what it needs to restore its vitality, but we will not be able to hear the quiet voice, or feel the gentle impulse that is our intuition, so weakened are we by the prejudice and ignorance of our society and education, urging us towards the balancing corrective. So often we are given whispers telling us that we have to look at something, change our ways. But we ignore them, we don't listen. It is only when we get a huge shout – which is called 'illness' – that we take any notice. To maintain our health, maybe we should follow Hippocrates' advice from 2500 years ago: 'Let food be your medicine, let your medicine be your food.'

This is one of the uses of a colour reading: to help us restore our damaged intuition. The herbs we need, the foods and the right colours, even the right course of action, are out there. We just need to identify what exactly we need for our particular situation now. One sure way that we can, like the Indian, hear them speak to us is through the language of colour.

Beneficial Food Colours

◆ Red, orange and yellow foods are hot and stimulating.
◆ Green foods are alkaline. They promote balance within the body, and are a tonic for the system.
◆ Blue, indigo and purple foods are soothing and cooling.

The benefits of individual colours are:

Red: Lifts energy; dissipates lethargy and tiredness; expands the arteries; quickens the bloodflow.

Orange: Promotes optimism and change; helps lift grief and disappointment; eliminates stagnant food from the gut; strengthens the immune system.

Yellow: Encourages laughter, joy and fun; a natural laxative; eliminates all unwanted toxins; feeds the central nervous system; lifts depression.

Green: Improves physical stamina; alleviates apprehension, panic, and fear; alleviates nausea; herbs are a tonic for the entire system.

Blue: Promotes peace and relaxation; helps concentration; heals anxiety; strengthens capillaries; helps to lower blood pressure.

Indigo: Brings relief from insecurity; helps to restructure one's life positively; promotes growth of new tissue; alleviates eczema and bruising.

Purple: Promotes leadership; calms the emotionally erratic; beneficial for mental disorders; good for conditions of the eyes; helps activate spiritual awareness.

Water Solarisation – The Sunshine Drink

This method of drinking liquid sunshine can be taken at any time, and it is very useful for incorporating with other healing methods. The sun purifies the water and instils the sunlight. You can literally bottle the sun's force. Just place a bottle of clear water in the sun for one day. Sip this slowly. It is a wonderful natural rejuvenation that revitalises you. Its a way of drinking the brilliance. You can separate the individual colours of the spectrum too. The effects may be slow, but they will occur.

One advantage of this way of absorbing colour is that there are no complications from overdosing which can happen if you are exposed to a colour for too long.

A basic guide is to drink the red, orange and yellow water in the mornings, and the blue and purple in the afternoon. Green is best at lunchtime, but it can be used at any time.

WATER SOLARISATION

1 Fill a clear glass tumbler, glass jug or bottle with pure spring or filtered water. It is important to use a vessel made of glass.

2 Wrap the container in a sheet of cellophane, a spotlight filter or gel, or even coloured perspex, in the colour that you want the water to carry. The top does not have to be covered. Some colour therapists use more sophisticated coloured wrappings, but for home use, cellophane and the spotlight gels you can find at theatrical lighting stores are perfectly adequate.

3 Leave the glass in a position that allows the daylight to fall upon it; even 30 minutes will make a difference to the water. However, I recommend that it be exposed to the light for at least six hours before drinking. The longer the time it is exposed, the stronger the energy of the colour becomes.

◆ The red, orange and yellow should be sipped slowly.
◆ Yellow should not be taken after 6 p.m. as it can be too energising before bedtime, and on the bladder!
◆ Greens, blues and the colours above these in the spectrum can be drunk somewhat faster ... but never gulped.
◆ Do not solarise the water for longer than 12 hours. One experiment showed that when the water had been solarised with a colour for two days, it 'burned' when tasted.

◆ Note: it is possible to charge water using an artificial light, which is particularly useful in northern winters. To do this, you will have to find a spectrum electric light bulb. Once again, it may be easier to find this in a theatrical lighting store.

A good way of discovering your level of sensitivity to colour is to shut your eyes and first taste a glass of solarised water. Then take a sip of water from the same source without solarisation. Some people are able to notice a difference. (Just because you do not detect a difference does not mean that you will not benefit from the solarised water.) Some sensitive people can detect a difference after the water has been instilled with colour for just five minutes. Try it yourself. Then try after 20 minutes' exposure, and so on up to 12 hours.

FOOD CAN ALSO BE SOLARISED
Wrap the food in the coloured cellophane, or put it in a bowl with the colour gel over the top, and expose it to the light for some hours. A red apple can be made even redder this way!

Colour and Dieting

Weight loss or gain cannot help but be connected to the subject of food. Colour is helpful in maintaining a healthy body weight:

WEIGHT LOSS
The colour to use for weight loss is yellow.

◆ It hates to carry excess baggage.
◆ It promotes agility both of mind and body.

◆ Wear it when exercising: it keeps you moving and pepped up.
◆ Eat it as yellow food, drink it as solarised water, or as yellow fruit juice.
◆ Visualise and incorporate yellow breathing.

WEIGHT GAIN

Blues are the colours that encourage weight gain.

◆ Blue inhibits activity.
◆ It allows the calories to gather and put on flesh.
◆ Psychologically, it does everything quietly and with discretion.
◆ It creates the right emotional environment for your body to be given the chance to increase itself.

Wear it, eat it, drink it, visualise it, or use the blue coloured breath technique – or, follow the Rainbow Diet below.

The Rainbow Diet

The Rainbow Diet is simply a support system, enabling you to harmonise within. We often do a great deal of work on ourselves spiritually without using or harmonising our physical stamina, which could aid us and supply us with vitality and energy. The body is our temple, and as such we must attend to it. Use food. Regard it as having come from the divine light that became the ultimate spiritual nutrition. By using the Rainbow Diet we are working with nature, which will only encourage our endeavour to become fully aware.

The Rainbow Diet is a way to treat yourself to a colour holiday – regard it as a trip to a health farm!

◆ You can have a one-day treatment, a two-day (weekend) treatment or take a whole week.

◆ Whichever treatment you choose, clear the day so that you do not have to go out or rush around.

◆ Use the day to relax totally so that you can receive the benefits of colour.

◆ Get an easy book to read, or magazine, and take the phone off the hook. You're not at home to others. This day is yours.

These treatments help your body clear out toxins (the negative of colours). As well, your body will be receiving the pure hues of positive colour. It will be both detoxified and regenerated.

◆ **Note: If you have a medical condition or are in any doubt as to whether you should embark on any of these diets, please consult your doctor before you do.**

THE ONE-DAY TREATMENT

1 On rising, drink a glass of warm water with a slice of lemon in it.

2 Take a sea salt bath. Put a large spoonful of sea salt into a warm bath and soak for at least seven minutes. You can take a sea salt shower, if you prefer. Wet the skin first, and then rub the sea salt all over your body, and rinse.

   After your bath or shower, smooth on clear oil, the purest you can find, one with no added perfume. Any good health food shop will advise you on this.

3 Rainbow Breakfast: This is a deep cleanser and rejuvenator. Prepare a rainbow fruit salad for yourself. Use any mixed fruits that are available – preferably fresh. Dried fruits, such as prunes, apricots and figs, are perfectly

acceptable, mixed with fresh fruit items. Try to incorporate a coloured fruit, including skin, from each colour of the spectrum in your rainbow fruit salad. There is a reminder of the various coloured foods on page 144.

4 Lunch and dinner? The same as breakfast.

◆ If you need a snack mid-morning or mid-afternoon, have a banana and warm water.

◆ Clothes for the day should be only white, like a white dressing gown or track suit.

◆ Before retiring at night, bathe again in sea-salt to wash away the toxins that will have emerged onto your skin. Nightwear should also be white.

This day is not only a cleanser, it also attunes your body to the brilliance I have written about in The Psychology of Colour chapter.

By the end of the day your body will feel lighter. The rainbow fruit salad has introduced all the colours that are hidden in the white light.

◆ Throughout the day, drink as much pure water as you can – at least eight pints!

THE WEEKEND OR TWO-DAY TREATMENT

The best time for this is over a weekend, unless you are lucky enough to have some days free during the working week.

This treatment is the same as the one-day cleanse. However, in addition to the rainbow fruit salad, it incorporates a green and white soup for lunch and dinner. This soup is built around green vegetables and herbs. It can also include potatoes, onions and garlic which, being white, represent the brilliance. These are the only white vegetables allowed in this green soup. Use a vegetable stock, not a meat stock, for the liquid. If you add only water, it will make its own stock. White pepper can be used freely but use sea-salt sparingly. Help yourself to this on both days.

THE COMPLETE ONE-WEEK TREATMENT

Every day in the week has its own colour. Taking each colour in turn, start with red on Monday and follow through to purple on Sunday. Each day is given over to the appropriate colour plus green and white. Green is included because it goes with every colour. You are less likely to overdose on a colour if green is incorporated. It balances and maintains a stability within the system. While the body is working with the colour vibration of the day, green is detoxifying. It is also a great tonic. Make sure each day's food consists of 75 per cent of the colour of the day and 25 per cent of green and white. If you want to reduce the colour of the day, just replace it with green or white. You may notice that you just don't want to eat a lot of one day's colour because of physical or emotional imbalance. You may just want to try a one-colour day, which is fine but make sure that you do it on the appropriate day, i.e.: don't do a red Monday food on an indigo Saturday.

Day 1: Red Monday

◆ Wear only red clothes.
◆ Eat only red foods. These can include anything from bright red apples through the pinks of pomegranates and prawns to the dark red of beetroot.
◆ Every meal must incorporate the red colour. But no red meat, please! You can get your protein from red beans and fish such as salmon.
◆ Have a breakfast of red apples, raspberries and green grapes.

◆ Lunch and dinner: peppers, tomatoes, beetroot, red cabbage, red lettuce, radishes, seafood (pink/red only) – and add a green salad or green vegetable to at least one of these meals.

◆ Make yourself a green and white soup. The one-week green-and-white soup has more white vegetables added than the two-day soup. Any green vegetables, potatoes, parsnips, leeks, onions, celery, garlic, green or white herbs and seasoning can be added. The green and white soup can be eaten every day in unlimited amounts. Use sea salt sparingly.

◆ Drink as much clear water as feels comfortable.

◆ Drink fresh mint or peppermint tea, or Japanese green tea. Do not drink tea or coffee.

◆ The water you drink up to midday can be red solarised water.

◆ After midday, return to clear water.

◆ Also, take one glass of freshly-pressed fruit or vegetable juice in the colour of the day (beetroot, tomato, raspberry or red currant). This can be bought, but make sure it contains no sugar or additives.

◆ Use the Star-Breath Technique (on page 117) with red at least three times a day.

Day 2: Orange Tuesday

◆ Wear only orange clothes.

◆ Eat only orange foods. These can include peach coloured foods.

◆ Remember to have your greens as well as your green-and-white soup if you are feeling really hungry.

◆ Proteins must be orange in colour, such as pulses or tofu.

◆ Again, no tea or coffee but green or mint teas are allowed.

◆ Drink plenty of water. Orange solarised water can be taken up to but not after midday.

◆ Have a glass of freshly-pressed orange or carrot juice.

◆ Use the Star-Breath Technique (on page 117) with orange at least three times a day.

Day 3: Yellow Wednesday

◆ Wear only yellow clothes.

◆ Eat only yellow foods, plus the green foods.

◆ Have yellow pulses or tofu for protein.

◆ Follow the liquid diet component of a glass of freshly-pressed yellow fruit or vegetable juice, clear water, and the green or mint teas.

◆ Yellow solarised water can be taken up to but not after midday.

◆ Use the Star-Breath Technique (on page 117) with yellow at least three times a day.

Day 4: Green Thursday

◆ Wear only green clothes.

◆ Eat only green foods, no other colour, i.e., green fruits, green vegetables or salads, and of course your green-and-white soup.

◆ For protein, eat lentils or tofu.

◆ Follow the water, juice and mint tea programme.

◆ Green solarised water can be taken all day.

◆ Use the Star-Breath Technique (on page 117) with green at least three times a day.

Day 5: Blue Friday

◆ Wear only blue clothes.

◆ There are few blue foods. You can have a fruit salad made up of white fruit only such as lychees, pears and apples (skins removed) plus any blue fruits.

◆ Have any amount of green-and-white soup, plus green salad.

◆ This is a fruit and vegetable day, with white tofu and fish for protein.

◆ Remember the clear water, no tea or coffee, and green and mint teas only.

◆ Blue solarised water can be taken from morning up to bedtime.

◆ Use the Star-Breath Technique (on page 117) with blue at least three times a day.

Day 6: Indigo Saturday

◆ Wear only indigo clothes.

◆ Eat only indigo foods, plus green foods and the green-and-white soup.

◆ Eat protein in the form of oysters, white fish, caviar.

◆ Drink the clear water, no tea or coffee; peppermint, mint and Japanese green teas only.

◆ Indigo solarised water can be taken from midday onwards to bedtime.

◆ Use the Star-Breath Technique (on page 117) with indigo at least three times a day.

Day 7: Purple Sunday

◆ Wear only purple or violet clothes.

◆ Eat only purple foods – plums, aubergines – plus green foods and the green-and-white soup.

◆ For protein, eat fish or tofu.

◆ Drink the clear water, no tea or coffee; peppermint, mint and Japanese green teas only.

◆ Purple solarised water can be taken from midday onwards to bedtime.

◆ Use the Star Breath Technique (on page 117) with violet at least three times a day.

Food Personalities and Syndromes

We are what we eat in more ways than one. Observing the different coloured foods we consume over a period of time can give vital clues as to how the food's colour vibration governs our everyday activities, including our health and personality.

It is essential to obtain an internal balance within our bodies. This in turn creates harmony hormonally within the nervous system. Not only does our psychic prowess improve, but we acquire a more balanced behaviour. In other words, the material and spiritual aspects within us become compatible, enabling us to make future plans for ourselves from a grounded, enlightened disposition.

The aim of this outline is to identify which colour syndrome you most relate to. Each specific food category pinpoints the main foods consumed that are unbalanced, causing the body to be acid or alkaline. Too much either way creates disharmony. This is followed by a list of foods that will help to correct imbalances.

The personality section highlights basic emotional patterns of behaviour with a section indicating the occupations that appeal to the person, plus a given body shape.

There are physical ailments relating to the food syndrome, with a healing colour given that can be introduced into the system using the various ways outlined in the book.

Three out of four indicators in any given category will be sufficient to put you in that particular bracket. You may find that you identify with two areas in one section and two in another: check The Psychology of Colour chapter to clarify which one you truly relate to.

FOOD PERSONALITIES AND SYNDROMES

1 Brown Rice Brigade (System: Acid)

◆ Personality: underdeveloped potential. This person is prone to repressed emotions. They are solid in temperament, the salt of the earth, but inclined to hide in the wings and never get on to the stage of life. They never let anyone down, which can make them a doormat.

◆ Main foods consumed (unbalanced): Meat – offal – bread – chocolate – beer.

◆ Corrective food: Brown rice – seeds – nuts – green vegetables.

◆ Occupation: Bank manager, as they love order and need a safe haven. Prefer being employed to being independent.

◆ Body shape: No curves or waist. Usually solid with thick ankles and wrists. Tough, rigid skin.

◆ Physical ailments: Acid indigestion. Brain disorders. Inclined to pneumonia and gall bladder problems.

◆ Healing colour: Bright blue.

2 White Nipple Necessity (System: Acid)

◆ Personality: Insecure. Dependent on others. Try very hard but are anxious and fearful of the future. Find it difficult to focus for long but have an expansive, creative imagination.

◆ Main foods consumed (unbalanced): Dairy products – milk – cheese – cream – sugar.

◆ Corrective Food: Quinoa – orange lentils – curry – algae – tomatoes.

◆ Occupation: All mundane jobs. The storekeeper – co-operative worker – schoolteacher. The unpaid social worker.

◆ Body shape: Loose flexible muscles. Usually flabby and fleshy. Inclined to weight gain.

◆ Physical ailments: Prone to diabetes – varicose veins – stomach ulcers – asthma – diverticulitis.
◆ Healing colour: Crimson red.

3 Green Consumption (System: Alkaline)

◆ Personality: A 'monkey' mentality, skipping all over the place. Light, easy-going personality, unable to earth itself. Always have their heads in the clouds. Sexually repressed.
◆ Main foods consumed (unbalanced): Salads – vegetables and fruit only.
◆ Corrective food: Millet – squash – oats – nuts – seeds – kidney beans.
◆ Occupation: Communes – tree conservationists – conscientious objectors. Not drawn to 9–5 commuter work.
◆ Body shape: Thin and weedy. Long arms. Weak constitution and delicate.
◆ Physical ailments: Lung and chest problems – arthritis – kidney stones – eye ailments.
◆ Healing colour: Peachy orange.

4 The Red Ripper (System: Acid)

◆ Personality: Aggressive to others. Impatient and irritable. Extremely self-assertive, pushing aside anything that may hinder progress of the self. Loves order. The pioneers of the world.
◆ Main foods consumed (unbalanced): Red meats – seafood – eggs – salt.
◆ Corrective food: Green vegetables – asparagus – grains – seeds and nuts.
◆ Occupation: Armed forces – any big organisations that require guts and nerve on the part of their employees. Heavy industry. Challenge seekers.
◆ Body shape: Wiry, hard, muscular. Stocky and strong.

◆ Physical ailments: Gout – appendicitis – headaches – liver – jaundice.

◆ Healing colour: Amethyst purple.

Coloured Foods and Drinks

◆ *Brilliance:* Nature's way of having us take in brilliance is by providing us with streams of pure, clear water. Water is liquid brilliance; bathing in a waterfall is the equivalent of standing under a cascade of clear light.

◆ *White foods:* The white food par excellence is seafood. But there are also white radish, parsnips, Jerusalem artichokes, lychees, garlic, onions, leeks, celery, potatoes, vanilla, rice, tofu and egg white.

◆ *Red foods:* Red meats, red peppers, red-skinned apples, tomatoes, radishes, red lettuce, beetroot, redcurrants, raspberries, strawberries, watermelon and red spices.

◆ *Orange foods:* Oranges, carrots, tangerines, apricots, peaches, swedes and sweet potato. Have a bowl of oranges on the table as a focal point.

◆ *Brown foods:* Nuts, mushrooms, brown rice, many of the herbs & spices (such as nutmeg and ground ginger), sultanas, dates, cereals – any food, or skin or shell, that has the brown Mother Earth colour.

◆ *Yellow foods:* Fresh ginger, golden syrup, honeydew melon, yellow plums, peppers and cherries, lemons, grapefruit, bananas, pineapple, sweetcorn, star fruit.

◆ *Gold foods:* Mangoes, some melons and paw paw. Indians eat gold leaf in some desserts.

◆ *Turquoise foods:* There are no purely turquoise foods but combinations of green, yellow and blue foods (skins included) can be eaten.

◆ *Green foods:* Salads, green leafy vegetables, green fruits –

kiwi fruit, greengages, gooseberries, apples, limes, etc. – pistachio nuts, avocado, green lentils, peas and green peppers.

◆ *Blue foods:* Blueberries, blue plums, bilberries, the herb flower borage.

◆ *Indigo foods:* Indigo-skinned grapes and plums, damsons, bilberries.

◆ *Purple foods:* Aubergines, purple grapes and plums, passion fruit, fresh figs.

◆ *Grey foods:* Any food that is going grey is lifeless and off – its life-energy is waning.

◆ *Silver foods:* Silver-coated sugared almonds, silverleaf cake and dessert decorations.

◆ *Black foods:* Licorice, black pepper, black olives, caviar, prunes, blackcurrants, blackberries and black truffles.

7

the psychology of colour

This section is an ABC of colour. Most of us have not been fortunate enough to be taught the language of colour as we were the alphabet and how to read at school. However, I know that the alphabet and words of colour can be learnt. Of course, what you create with them is where the art of colour comes in. What I have tried to do is to use words to create a wash of colour that will draw the reader into its magic.

Each colour has many facets. In fact, this section could just as easily be called 'The Many Faces of Colour'. Each colour of the spectrum has its own level of consciousness. As we go up the spectrum taking red as the base colour, we leave the slower, denser vibrations of the material world, the reds, oranges and yellows, and enter the finer, quicker vibrations of the mental and spiritual – the blues, indigos and purples. Green is the balancer, the divider between the two. It is made up of aspects of each side – yellow, from the magnetic end and blue from the electrical end.

Blue is often thought of as being more 'spiritual' than red. This is a misunderstanding. The person who climbs to the top of Mount Everest has just as much spirituality as the priest in his church. All colours are spiritual, but each colour has a different way of manifesting its own spirituality.

Each colour has a different wavelength and frequency. The act of intuiting colour is like tuning in to a particular channel on your television. Only when you are tuned to the correct wavelength can you get a clear picture. Every colour is strong, but each colour's strength differs from that of any other colour. Blue's strength lies in the fact that it will consider the situation first and look before it leaps, whereas red will charge in without a second thought, a strength in its own right.

The point of working with the psychology of colour is to seek out the positive aspects of each hue. You need not be afraid of or shun the negative or lower aspects of a colour. They are there to help you. The dark aspects show what needs to be attended to, and the aim is to achieve a balance.

Each colour section is arranged in the same way, giving the principal colour's polarity, positive and negative keywords, general qualities and characteristics; also, information about its different shades and tints, where they exist. Spend time with the first section on brilliance, because it is the light from which all the colours come. Be aware that your introduction to colours will be the experience of feeling pure sunlight physically on your body, but on another level, you will be tapping in to the universal intelligence. It will be the closest you can get cosmically to feeling cosmic force. You can just dip into a section to get an instant aspect of a colour, but read them from beginning to end to get the total experience.

The language of colour is a tool of self-discovery. If you feel drawn to a particular colour it may indicate a deep need within you for something which that colour vibration holds within itself. Light is the whole; the colours it diffracts into are individual personalities, and each speaks with an individual voice and has its own point of view. There are blue statements and green statements, orange statements and black statements. This is the language of colour that you need to listen for – with your eyes! No colour is 'right'; no colour is 'wrong'. By learning the language of colour you will be able to appreciate the entire spectrum of meanings and inform-ation the intelligence of light is giving you through colour. Just by reading the pages on each colour you open yourself to the influence of that vibration. The best way to do this is to read about them in a slightly meditative frame of mind. Suspend the critical faculty and let the colour permeate your being. Colours reflect to you the fine inner echoes of yourself.

Close your eyes and visualise the colour you are going to read about. Swamp yourself with this colour and breathe it in. Open your eyes, and as you start to read, keep the colour in mind so that it stays with you while you read that section. By reading a section you not only gain knowledge, but actually begin to experience a feel for the colour. Try smelling and tast-ing the colour! This will enable you to recognise the subtle and obvious difference on a psychic level. Remember, colour is experienced directly. It does not have to pass through the intellect and be scrutinised to see if it makes 'sense'. It is an immediate experience.

Let your imagination wander into the land of colour. You will find that the sun paints its lessons on all things.

brilliance

'When you can see nothing then you can see everything because nothing is something.'

The Art of Happy Living, His Holiness Param Sant

Transparency.
Brilliance is the supreme ray;
the ray of rays.
Brilliance brings all rays of colour
into perfect balance.
The number of brilliance is thirteen,
which shows that it has the power
to pierce through death
and resurrection.
Many people mistake brilliance for white.
Brilliance is the light from whence
all other colours spring,
and return into.
Light is the whole.
The colours it diffracts into are individual personalities
and each speaks with an individual voice.
Brilliance is not
actually a colour: it is the original light.
It is not an Earthly colour: it is cosmic light.
Brilliance represents the universal intelligence.
It has the purity of the trinity of love,
power and wisdom.
Brilliance's positivity is simplicity in all things.
It is just being.
Brilliance's negativity is when we feel lost, invisible,
or in a vacuum;
the complications of life.

Our local source of brilliance is the sun.
Without brilliance there is no vision.
Brilliance cuts directly through to the truth.
It clears the way for necessary actions.
Brilliance clears any cloudiness in a person or colour.
When we say that a person is brilliant,
we are acknowledging his or her
purity of vision and action.
Brilliance is transparent; it can see
right through you.
Brilliance adds lustre and beauty.
Look at the light coming from a diamond.
Add a touch of brilliance to any colour
and it will become brighter.
Brilliance is the hard light that exposes all
flaws, shams and corruptions.
Brilliance is the reality of life.
Brilliance contains the essence of all qualities, both
positive and negative, sparkling
in the brilliance of
perfection.
Light
sustains our life.
Our expression of someone
being 'off-colour' is literally true.
We can see that the light in the person
is muddied or diluted in some way.
If the light disappears entirely,
the person is dead.
No light, no life.
When I want to restore a person's vibrancy,
I will put them in pure light.
Or simply tell them to go for a walk in the sunlight.

Two weeks on a Greek island
being flooded with the sun's brilliance
does wonders for body,
soul and psyche.
A little touch of brilliance goes a long way.
And we will go a long way for a
touch of brilliance.
Light is a nutrient and it is vital and necessary for
perfect health.
Brilliance is there in the wisdom that brings the
universe into a state of perfection.
It is pure spirit and conscious perfection.
Brilliance
is the clear light
that *The Tibetan Book of The Dead*
advises the newly-dead person to head for ...
It is the clear light
at the end of the tunnel
that people report from
their near-death
experiences.

'(Man) is an object which views the light while in light.'

His Holiness Param Sant

white

'Cleanliness is, indeed, next to Godliness.'
John Wesley

white polarity
Virgin – sullied

positive white keywords
Pristine; completeness; all-giving; openness;
unity; exposes the hidden and untrue.

negative white keywords
Isolation; sterility; stark; frustration;
starchiness; prissiness; boring.

White is a denser brilliance.
White is what is left when
the brilliance has been taken out.
White has a density.
If you hold up a transparent crystal,
you are looking at clear brilliance.
If you hold up a white cotton sheet you
cannot see through it.
White has just stepped down from the
ultimate purity of brilliance.
Thus the bride wears white at her wedding
to symbolise purity in human form.
White contains an equal balance of all the
colours of the spectrum.
White is a combination of all the colours.
As such, white can both show a need to,

and be used to, combine.
Hold a handful of snow up to the sunlight and you
will see minute flashes of all the colours
of the rainbow sparkling away.
White's fundamental quality is equality.
All colours are equal in white.
In mythology white is a symbol of unity.
White seeks to be fair.
The judge's white wig on his head
symbolises his impartiality.
White is the spiritual saver.
All will be well when white is about.
The white knight
on his charger rescuing maidens...
The doctor in his white coat rescuing
us from dragon death ...
Hopalong Cassidy wearing his
white hat and riding his white horse ...
White shows up in the nick of time.
White encourages.
It helps bring us through times
of stress and strain.
White is next to the cosmic intelligence of brilliance,
so, while white has faith, it is not blind faith.
White derives its faith from reason;
even when it cannot explain
the reason for its faith.
As the French philosopher Blaise Pascal puts it:
'The heart has reasons that Reason knows not of.'
This is the faith of the missionary who
continues his divine mission
against all odds, and
even unto death.

White is expansive and creative.
It is the perfectly fair field against
which all things may manifest.
White is efficient.
It is clean, and unruffled.
However, too much white causes frustration,
isolation and a feeling
of emptiness.
All white décor creates an atmosphere of sterility.
It provides little stimulation for the senses.
Hospital rooms should never be all-white.
It may get rid of the germs,
but it also depletes
the human psyche.
For the same reason, a baby's nursery
should never be just white.
Peaches, pinks and creams will
make the occupant feel
warm and welcome.
All colours throw out heat, but white
throws out the least.
White reflects all the colours, therefore
it is the coolest colour.
So tropical countries favour white for clothes
and the interiors of houses.
White is the perfection of all colours.
It is completeness, yet it holds nothing in.
White is the great opener.
Because white is closer to the brilliance than
any other colour, it has the ability
to bring hidden things
out into the open.
'Pure as the driven snow.'

There is something inhuman about white.
The two whitest places on Earth are the
North and South Poles.
White is so close to brilliance that human life is unable to
survive there comfortably for long.
And yet human beings are drawn to
return to it again and again
for its purifying power.
White conjures up hope.
White is tranquillity
because everything is equal in white,
so white is the symbol of peace.
When someone raises the white flag, the
fighting ceases.
The first step towards living in that harmony
that the colours symbolise, living
side by side in peace, is white.

There are no shades or tints of white

From the inner light of rest
all colours are rising in white hope.

red

The Red Badge of Courage
Title of a novel by Stephen Crane

red polarity
Growth – destruction

positive red keywords
Leader; tenacious; fights for the right; creative; dynamic; perseverance; gratitude; reviver; cheerfulness.

negative red keywords
Physical violence; lustful; intolerant; cruel; destructive; warmonger; possessive; bullying; condemning; stubbornness; gracelessness; shame; guilt.

Red is the spirit of physical life.
Red is the colour of the base chakra – the will to live.
Red is power.
Red is fire and drive.
Red is adrenaline and will-power.
Red is going to get its own way, come what may.
Red is tireless energy.
Red likes to keep moving.
Red is the survival of the fittest.
The red signal of pain is Mother Nature's warning.
Red is territorial.
Our evolution on Earth would have been
impossible without red.
Red likes to be first.
Red is the liberator.

Red is courage.

Red's motto is: 'We will overcome.'

Red alerts you to danger.

Red is passionate.

Red believes with a passion.

It loves (or hates), passionately.

When red defends, it defends to the end.

Red is exciting.

Red is quickening.

When the mother feels the baby quickening in her
womb for the first time, this is a red action
on the baby's part.

Red is practical.

Red believes in action.

Red hates to hang about.

A red statement is: keep moving.

Even when it speaks, red speaks towards action.

Red gets the blood up.

It is essential for the circulation of the blood.

'The body is the blood thereof' – Leviticus

Red has a burning desire to get somewhere.

Red tends to act without thinking.

Red rag to a bull in a china shop.

Red is the pioneer.

Red pushes forwards against all odds.

Red is the irritant that keeps you moving
no matter what.

Red helps break the patterns of rigidity
that block our path.

Red puts you in the hot seat; it spurs you to get up
and go for it.

Red stimulates you and gives you the will-power
to continue.

Red recycles and renews the enthusiasm
to carry on.
Red is the conqueror.
Red is power; and the power to direct
the power.
Red was the colour of the Roman legions.
Rome's law and order marched across the
world behind its legions.
Red is sexuality.
Red is the mating energy and governs sexual relationships.
Red is amoral – all it is concerned with is
reproduction, continuing
the species.
In its sexual aspect,
red rather than religion is the opium of the people.
Red has sex out of true sexual desire.
Red at its best will give a
satisfying and passionate lovelife.
Red at its worst becomes bestial and perverse.
Red is goodwill to all men.
Red is a great rescuer.
It is the cavalry that charges in at the last minute
to save the wagon train.
Red seeks to make up for all that is missing.
Red believes in survival – self-preservation.
Red has a desire for justice.
But it is practical and will ensure that
justice is seen to be done.
If necessary, red will go to war to achieve justice –
the 'just war'.
Red brooks no obstacles.
Red is the reformer.
Red is the fiery force; it burns away impurities.

Red redeems.

Red can mean war.

Red is a great fighter.

Red must win.

If necessary, it will go to war to attain supremacy.

War can be red's answer to an argument,

particularly if red tempers are lost –

which can easily happen.

Red takes no prisoners when

its back is to the wall.

Red can become dictatorship.

Too much red can make the will

override the heart.

Red can be the warmonger with no

compassion for the loss of lives.

Red at its worst is the tyrant and

brutal murderer.

Red at its best is a fine leader of men.

Red is a born strategist.

Red is a lover of mankind

and will sacrifice itself for its fellow human beings.

The soldier who sacrifices his life for his comrades.

Red is the ego.

It loves having the red carpet rolled out.

Red has no hesitation in going public.

Red ego in its positive form is the belief

in the worth and value

of the self.

Red ego in its negative form is the inflated ego;

the bullfrog.

This red seeks advancement no matter

who or what suffers.

Frustrated, red ego can become extremely harsh,

rebellious and destructive.
Negative red can be pushy,
domineering and defiant.
If someone tramples on your toes to advance
themselves, they are likely to be working
in the negative red.
Red is insecure.
Negative red is shame and guilt.
Guilt is fear of failure.
Shame means: 'I am faulty.'
Red can be a show-off.
Red is a very noisy colour.
It wants your attention.
Science has shown the human
body to be a noisy vehicle.
Where the circulation is
good, the blood literally sings through
the veins.
If hindered by disease, it becomes
a sad, sullen murmur.
Red is a good colour to help someone face death.
Red removes fear.
Red overcomes lingering and reluctance
to move on.
'Time to move on' is the red view of dying!
Red encourages the person to see death as the
door to the new adventure.
Beautiful red flowers for the dying person
to gaze upon would be ideal.
Red has a burning desire to probe deeper.
It is the explorer with the energy of the
life force at its command.
Red is zest, energy and drive.

Red builds great things from very little.

It is the constructor.

From little acorns great oak trees grow.

THE MANY MOODS OF RED

There are many tones of red. They all have red's basic qualities, but are modified by whether they are a higher or lower octave to red itself. Red is the most dominant colour of the spectrum.

Scarlet, crimson and flame are all higher octaves of red. In general, they are the most active of the reds. After these, brown begins to enter the red and we have the shades russet red, maroon and dark red. These are more subdued and cautious. Then come the pinks. There are a host of pinks. They are worthy of a book of their own. Here I can only sketch in a few: cerise, rose, soft salmon pink, orchid and pink. The pinks are, as their hues suggest, much lighter and gentler than red. One obvious characteristic of all the pinks is that they are extremely feminine. The last of the red hues here is magenta – red plus blue.

It is important to be aware that the tints of any colour are considered to have positive characteristics. However, it is my experience that an overload of a tint can have negative side-effects. For instance, an overload of pink can produce the dominance of red. On the other hand, the shades of any colour are considered negative. But the negative can be useful! It tells us what we need to look at.

The difference between a shade and a tint is that a shade has *black* mixed with a colour, whereas a tint has *white* with a colour. The shades are darker and the tints are paler.

Scarlet – love of life; enthusiasm

◆ Scarlet is the highest octave of red.

◆ Scarlet seems brighter and richer than pure red.
◆ Scarlet is red with bells on. Inspirational entrepreneurs, speculators and originators work with scarlet in their make-up.
◆ Scarlet-driven people not only climb the mountain, they must climb the highest mountain.
◆ Scarlet has a strong sexual drive.

Good examples: Edmund Hillary (first climber to reach the top of Mount Everest); St Joan of Arc; Boadicea.

Problem: More inner conflict than most, lack of scruples.

Crimson – peaceful strength; determination; liberation
◆ Crimson is also a high vibration of red.
◆ Crimson has a touch of blue in it.
◆ For crimson, life is to be loved, not overcome.
◆ It does not believe in struggle – it believes in going and getting what it wants.
◆ Nothing daunts crimson.
◆ Crimson is concerned with the individual rather than the mass.
◆ Crimson is extremely forthright.

Good examples: Moses; Duke of Edinburgh.

Problems: Impulsiveness and unpredictability.

Flame – cauterising
◆ Flame is a medium octave of red.
◆ Flame has licks of bright yellow in it.
◆ Flame generates new life by force or fury: 'I burn through.'
◆ It cleanses by fire.
◆ Great zeal.
◆ Flame red keeps going no matter what.
◆ It probes deeply.
◆ Guts and fire.

◆ It begins a new spiritual phase in life, the whole being having been regenerated.

Good examples: The Avenging Angel; Winston Churchill.

Problems: Too hot in its zeal; leaves the ground scorched and barren.

Russet Red – knowledge with wisdom

◆ A mixture of brown and red.

◆ Russet red has a quiet confidence, an enthusiasm that does not draw attention to itself.

Good examples: The backroom boys; the inventor; Jane Austen.

Problems: Lack of direction; impractical in worldly matters.

Maroon – deep thought; breaking through

◆ Maroon has will and power from the red plus the deep thought and quiet understanding of the touch of brown.

◆ Maroon shows overcoming a time of great sorrow. It is saying, 'We have come through.'

Good examples: the Beirut hostages.

Problems: Can stay stuck in old sorrow, feeling persecuted.

Dark Red – the vampire; the lecher

◆ Dark red can become inert through hopelessness. Dark red believes in the old Arab saying 'God gives nuts to monkeys with no teeth', so 'what's the use?' is the familiar cry of dark red.

◆ Dark red can be over-indulgent on all levels, particularly in sex.

◆ It can be the ambitious bully.

◆ Dark red can be brutally cruel, even murderous when thwarted. One aspect of dark red can be cruelty to animals.

◆ This colour is connected to congealed blood.

Bad examples: Pimps, sex molesters.

Problem: Stagnancy.

THE PINKS

Cerise – womanhood; ripeness; friendliness

I have noticed that whenever I wear cerise, a blend of rich rose and lilac colours, everyone comes and talks to me, and becomes very open, warm and friendly.

◆ Cerise is the woman who has got it and knows she's got it ... and everybody else knows she's got it.

◆ The woman in cerise separates the men from the boys.

◆ Men don't wear cerise – at least not on the outside..

Good examples: Sophia Loren; Joan Collins.

Problems: Too available; flaunting oneself.

Rose Pink – spiritual beauty; universal love; compassion

Rose pink prepares the way for all treatments. It relaxes the physical body and helps us to receive. It prepares us to respond.

◆ The essence of rose pink is full bloom; maturity.

◆ A very feminine colour: rose pink states that a woman is ready to have what a mature woman wants. When a man is in his rose pink stage he is 'distinguished'. It is not a colour for teenage girls.

◆ Rose pink has healing beauty.

◆ It has beauty that expands, that extends beyond the physical.

◆ It is the in-breath of the breathing cycle.

◆ Rose pink is a constant affection, faithful, forgiving: the true love that we are all searching for.

◆ It is fulfilment of potential.

◆ It is the colour of support when betrayed or let down.

Good example: The Madonna.
Problems: Immaturity and blind trust; impetuousness.

Soft Salmon Pink – love of humanity

◆ Salmon is pink and brown.
◆ The pink side of it is very concerned with love, and the brown puts a curb on the pink.
◆ Salmon is high affection, affection without ulterior motive.
◆ It is sensible love.
◆ The man in the salmon pink shirt is saying: 'I am sensual.' But love life with him may be on ration ... salmon pink doesn't give it away easily.

Good examples: the bachelor at 50; the sexual tease.
Problems: Over-cautious in love, the 'I'm not ready yet' syndrome.

Orchid – individual; rare; unconventional

◆ This lovely lavender-blue-pink indicates the one and only; individuality. Thus, the significance of giving an orchid to one's beloved.
◆ If you are drawn to orchid, it shows that you are doing things your way, and that its a 'one-off' only course. But the negative side is you must take care not to become waxen and immobile.
◆ No one else does anything in quite the same way as an orchid pink person. They are rare, just like the orchid. You stumble upon it in a jungle and just one word describes the tint: paradise.

Good examples: Jesus Christ; Mother Teresa.
Problems: Too exotic; an all-or-nothing attitude; stiff.

Pink – hope; receptive; intimate

◆ Pink is red with white.

◆ Pink is romantic.

◆ Pink is affection.

◆ Pink is kindness.

◆ The paler it goes the wider, higher and deeper the love extends.

◆ Pale pink is highly sensitive. It says, 'We'll meet again.'

◆ Pink warmth melts and dissolves.

◆ Pink is comforting; it mollifies.

◆ Pink is the colour of the peace offering. Pour pink on troubled waters.

◆ Pink is great in a crisis: if you're being mugged, think pink!

◆ Use pink after a person has been assaulted in any way; or if they have had part of their body removed in an operation.

◆ Pink gets rid of hang-ups.

◆ Pink is like a magnet, it draws and attracts.

◆ A new-born baby is born in the pink and, as it develops into adulthood, it becomes a naughty nude.

◆ A young person drawn to pink can be showing that they are now ready to develop their full potential.

◆ Pink is wonderful in the mid-life crisis when the dissolution of old patterns and reassessment is imperative.

◆ An older women drawn to pale pink can be showing that she has unrealistic expectations – she may be still waiting for her unrealised girlhood dreams to come true. Pink will help her to reassess. It is time to let old ideas and issues melt away.

◆ Too much pink shows a need for protection.

◆ Pink aids the digestion: affection is nourishment.

◆ Baby pink says: 'I need nurturing and taking care of.'

◆ Pink is universal harmony. It is unconditional love.

◆ When we are truly 'in the pink', we can fall in love again, again, and again.

◆ It is said: 'To love another person is to see the face of God.'

Good example: Marilyn Monroe.

Problems: Too much pink indicates a desire to dominate and control; sentimentality; becoming too soft and silly; too emotional.

Magenta – the great improver

◆ Magenta is red and purple.

◆ Magenta wields the invisible energies of infra-red and ultra-violet.

◆ Magenta's powers are not fully seen.

◆ It is spiritually uplifting.

◆ In the presence of magenta, one feels better.

◆ The magenta person seems to know what you are thinking and feeling.

◆ Magenta creates achievement through love.

◆ It takes the tender approach to getting what it wants.

◆ It helps recovery from sorrow with dignity rather than distraught expressions of emotion.

◆ Magenta is the arbiter; it stands between antagonists and attempts to bring them to peace and a common under-standing.

◆ Magenta knows that 'I can have my way, but not always. I must let others have their way, too.'

◆ It accepts that 'things are the way they are.'

◆ However, magenta is often caught in the past-was-better-than-the-present syndrome.

◆ Magenta is the greatest organiser of them all.

Good examples: The United Nations; Abraham Lincoln.

Problems: Indifference and disinterest; impersonal; slapdash.

> **'While we are talking, envious time is fleeing:**
> **Seize the day, put no trust in the future.'**
>
> Quintus Horatius Flaccus (Roman poet)

orange

'The more things change, the more they stay the same.'
Henry V, Shakespeare

orange polarity
Activity – laziness

positive orange keywords
Strength; flamboyance; warm-hearted; generous;
tolerant; excitement; untiring energy; fearlessness;
sociable; just; freedom.

negative orange keywords
Over-proud; pessimistic; overbearing; exhibitionist;
sponging; self-indulgent; misleading.

Orange is assimilation.
Orange is our gut instincts.
Orange is the colour of the sacral chakra.
It is the ability to be free, to explore.
Orange is focused on the physical necessities of life.
Orange is taking for oneself what is needed.
Orange draws towards itself.
Orange is self-reliance.
Orange is practical knowledge.
Orange is physical intuition.
Sportsmen relate to the colour orange.
In its role of assimilator, orange is our
intestinal laboratory.
It tests, and accepts
or rejects.

Orange has impetus.

Orange is extremely persistent.

But where red bullies, orange bides its time.

Orange is the great rejuvenator.

Orange is optimistic.

Orange is positive.

Orange is genial.

It is tolerant and warm-hearted.

Orange is friendship.

It is the life and soul of the party.

Orange is the practical joker.

Orange has mental vigour.

It unfolds the mentality.

Orange has the power to illuminate
through creative activity.

Orange loves to cook.

Orange sees the whole ... and develops the whole.

It is very constructive.

It's the get-it-together-again colour.

Orange is expansion.

It breaks down barriers.

Orange shatters.

It breaks open blocks which then causes
a freeing action.

The breakthrough of orange frees the spirit.

Orange broadens life and is very purposeful.

Orange moves on.

It is the colour of divorce!

Whatever red is, orange will be, but without
the aggressive force.

Orange has strength,
but not the physical strength of red.

Orange strength is more subtle.

It stimulates gently.
Orange believes in the community.
It likes social gatherings.
It loves to use the telephone.
Orange is party time.
Orange likes
to work in groups.
It has pride in the achievement
of the group rather than in
its own success.
Negative orange has an inferiority complex.
Orange is benign.
An overload of orange can restrict and make rigid.
Orange can eradicate.
It brings up the energy of past events that
need to be assimilated so that they can be completed.
Orange will not let sleeping dogs lie.
Orange is the most rejected colour in our time.
An aversion to orange
could point to deep feelings of outrage at having
been cruelly treated.
An aversion to orange
could indicate someone holding
themselves back socially – particularly in
business gatherings, office parties, meetings, and so on.
Orange gives the courage to face the consequences.
It accepts what is ... and then changes it.
Orange knows that change for change's sake
is not necessarily change for the better.
Change is not always visible.

THE MANY MOODS OF ORANGE
Shades and Tints

Dark Orange – opportunist
◆ A person relating to dark orange feels thwarted.
◆ Ambition is the downfall of dark orange; it tries too hard. The person who assures you they can do it when you know they can't.
◆ Dark orange usually has a chip on his shoulder.
◆ A dark orange person might say: 'I'm going to be a brain surgeon', when he has never finished school.
◆ Dark orange can do more harm than good.
◆ Dark orange is a compulsive hoarder.

Good examples: The addicted gambler; Inspector Clouseau in the *Pink Panther* films.

Problems: Not understanding the reality of their potential (or lack of potential); the outcast.

Amber – progressive; supportive strength
◆ Amber removes doubt and suspicion, and gives confidence.
◆ The amber personality is very willing and tries everything.
◆ Amber helps one trust one's own judgement.
◆ Give amber to a doubting Thomas.
◆ Amber promotes quiet activity. It is the colour of mental vigour.
◆ Amber sheds light in dark places. It is the colour of realisations and understandings.

Good example: Band Aid concert's organiser, Bob Geldof.

Problems: Jack-of-all-trades, master of none; restlessness.

Peach – gentle persuasion
◆ Peach has all the qualities of orange without the impetus.
◆ Peach walks instead of runs.

◆ Peach encourages communication.

◆ Peach is a flow of movement: in-breathing/out-breathing in perfect harmony.

◆ Peach creates a safe environment for confronting difficult or painful memories.

◆ It is good when working with teenagers who have no idea what they are going to do with their lives.

◆ Peach assures us that things will be all right.

◆ Orange makes us jump; peach tells us if it is safe to jump.

◆ Peach is cautious.

◆ Peach can find out that it is giving out love for no return.

Good examples: Mothers and elders; the perfect gentleman.

Problems: Evading; putting off until tomorrow.

'I make the most of all that comes
And least of all that goes.'

The Philosopher, Sara Teasdale

brown

'And you all know security is mortal's chiefest enemy.'
Macbeth, Shakespeare

brown polarity
Accretion – decay

positive brown keywords
Solidity; reliability; moderation; sober; self-assurance;
caring; confidentiality; loyal.

negative brown keywords
Self-doubt; withdrawal; depression; frustration;
discontentment; barren; obsession with decay.

Brown is absorption and solidarity.
Brown is reliable.
Brown is down-to-earth.
Brown is capable; it copes.
Brown is as safe as houses.
Brown is the salt of the earth.
Brown is the colour of conservation.
Brown is calm, and calming.
It is the colour of moderation.
Above all, brown is stable.
Not too much excitement about brown, perhaps,
but much plain, common sense.
Brown loves to be safe.
Being safe is brown's passion.
Brown will have a modest manner.
Brown goes about life with a quiet assurance.

There is still a touch of red in brown.
Brown is a slow but sure developer.
Brown holds its own counsel.
Brown has to understand before acting.
It doesn't take chances.
When the euphoria is rising and the castles
are building up high in the sky,
brown sobers things up.
Brown is the deep thinker.
Brown understands that
there is more to life than one can see.
The person working with the brown vibration
is deeply studious.
Brown is the swot.
Brown is single-minded.
It will often be found deep in thought.
Brown can fathom out where things went wrong.
It has depths of concentration.
Brown contemplates with quiet confidence.
Brown is four-square.
If you are
seeking to employ someone
reliable, loyal and steady and a candidate
turns up for the
interview wearing brown,
this may be your man.
Or woman.
Brown will not let you down.
It will follow your instructions to the letter.
Those under the influence of brown are capable
of being your right-hand man.
Or woman.
Brown will hold the fort while you are away

without plotting to get your position,
and relinquish it gladly when
you come back.
Brown does not desire the spotlight.
It is quite happy for someone else
to be in command.
Brown likes to work behind the scenes.
To be found off-stage, waiting in the wings.
Brown marks time.
Brown is often waiting for the right moment –
which never comes.
If you need a pushy salesman,
brown is not your man.
Brown hates any kind of
bartering or wheeler-dealing.
Working for an established institution
suits brown best.
Brown is the colour of striving hard to do well.
Brown's personal life can be quite hard.
It often experiences life as
a bit of a struggle.
Brown can become so absorbed in work
that it becomes single-minded to an extreme.
This can lead brown to withdraw within.
There is often suffering from painful conditions and
problems that
brown feels nothing and no one can solve.
This can sometimes make brown retreat inwards.
Depression sets in and brown becomes
consumed with an obsession with
the decay of life.
Brown doesn't like travel much.
It prefers to stay in its own environment.

Brown feels safer when it, and the world
around it, is settled
and steady.
Brown dislikes having the order of its life disrupted –
as Goldilocks found when she visited the
Three Brown Bears.
Brown is the colour of the earth.
Most animals are brown.
Brown can hide its light under a bushel.
Brown has hidden potential.
Brown
is the seed in
the husk, afraid to
burst forth and pop up
from below the ground so that
it can develop its full potential.
Brown needs the nurturing of
the pinks and gold
to develop
trust.
Brown has the power to recycle – it knows it will return.
Brown likes to appear solid.
It can even refuse to allow itself to be ill as this
is a sign of weakness.
Brown can have a deep fear of the process of decay.
Thus, it is unable to allow the breakdown phase
of the growth-decay cycle
to take place.
Brown has it all – potentially.
Brown desperately seeks consistency.
But brown also has a fear of life itself – and of
claiming its full due.
This is the costly side of brown's quietness, reliability

and willingness to take a back seat.
Out of its own yearning to be safe, brown
tries to make others safe.
But this safety is often bought at the expense of life.
Brown tries to make life safe by keeping it
still and static.
Dogged by fear, with an irresistible need to be safe
and secure, rather than go out and face
whatever seems to be the problem,
brown tends to
dig in.
Which may be why
brown is the colour of hibernation.

THE MANY MOODS OF BROWN
Shades and Tints

Dark Brown – self-centred; biased
◆ In some ways, dark brown is simply the negative of brown.
◆ Dark brown cares nothing for anyone else's opinion. As such, it is associated with selfishness of all kinds.
◆ It is the person who cuts back on a company's finances; it reduces.
◆ Dark brown also has a fear of being buried alive.
◆ However, there is a positive side to dark brown: history. History is 'dead and buried'. This is the black in dark brown. It is all our yesterdays. But history is also a resource, in the light of which we can consider our current situation. History brown; it is the manure that fertilises and prepares the ground.
◆ Dark brown is earth's oven. There is always something cooking.
◆ Dark brown also knows it has the secret of rebirthing:

everything reverts back to the soil. Sick soil = diseased people.

Good examples: The doctor of the soil – the farmer; earthquake.

Problems: Stasis, unable to break down.

Rich Russet Brown: quiet assurance; intuition; concentration

◆ Things move a little faster with rich russet brown.

◆ This is the basic colour of most orders of monks. Contrary to their modern image, monks were hard-working, earthy people. They personify the 'activity with restraint' of russet brown. This colour has an intuitive trust in the order of things on earth.

Good example: St Francis.

Problems: Superstition; secretiveness.

Browny Pink – stable affection

◆ The brown element in browny pink will give single-mindedness, while the pink gives love and affection.

◆ This is summed up in the traditional Italian mama who is Mother Earth to her family, but doesn't concern herself with the outside world. She takes care of her own patch of ground.

Good example: The Italian mama.

Problems: Selfishness; blinkered.

Stone – intuition; clairvoyance

◆ Stone is a tint of brown.

◆ It is less heavy, so the aspect of the intuition is clearer.

◆ Stone shuns glamour and glory.

◆ It is the medium or clairvoyant, working away quietly at home.

◆ Stone is the people of any country. Without the backbone

of the ordinary person, there would be nothing for the politicians to parade in front of.

◆ Stone is the audience.

Good example: The dedicated nurse.

Problem: Inclined to become a dormouse in life; no personal identity.

Cream: softness

◆ Cream softens.

◆ As every interior decorator knows, cream softens a space – but at the same time enlivens it.

◆ Cream brings an expansion of the space.

◆ The Spartan quality of the white is warmed by the brown.

◆ The white provides a safety net that allows you to face the decay side of the recycling process that is an aspect of brown.

◆ Cream compensates and helps one appreciate what is.

◆ Cream gives the reassurance that whatever happens, you will be all right.

Good examples: The psychiatrist; the sincere friend.

Problems: Slackness; dribbling; senility.

Coppery Bronze: flowingness; balance

◆ Coppery bronze encourages quick passage with the minimum of disruption.

◆ All secret services relate to this colour.

◆ Copper pans and pots are prized for their ability both to allow the heat through with the minimum of resistance and to spread the heat evenly. It absorbs – as do copper bracelets worn on the wrist against rheumatism.

◆ It takes away acidity; it is nature's sweetener; it pours oil on troubled waters.

◆ Coppery bronze represents quiet but effective activity.

- It has several colours in it, which is why it has multiple aspects.
- Coppery bronze activates the understanding that allows personal change to take place without dramatic displays.

Good example: Marriage guidance counsellor.

Problem: Playing the 'fixer'.

'A bird in the hand is worth two in the bush.'

Anonymous

yellow

'All things be ready if our minds be so.'

Henry V, Shakespeare

yellow polarity

Wisdom – stupidity

positive yellow keywords

Quickness; mental agility; joy; originality; rigor; expansion; perceptive; tolerant; probing; honesty; justice; confident.

negative yellow keywords

Analytical; acidic; sarcastic; treacherous; absent-minded; ignorant; intellectually rigid; chatterbox; critical; impatient; judgmental; vague; folly.

Yellow is the mind.

Yellow is control through the intellect.

Yellow is known as the ray of mental wisdom.

Yellow is the colour of the solar plexus chakra.

Yellow is the colour of the scientist.

Yellow is inquisitive.

It unravels and reveals.

Yellow leaves no stone unturned.

Yellow helps think through difficulties

and will explore all avenues.

Yellow is the brightest colour of the spectrum.

Yellow is flexible and adaptable.

Yellow is penetrating.

Yellow is the concentration

that gets through to the

core of the matter.
Yellow desires to learn.
Yellow is smart.
Yellow is clarity of thought.
Yellow is precise.
Yellow is very clear about life ...
and still optimistic.
Yellow is continually striving.
Yellow is information.
Yellow is civilisation.
Yellow focuses attention.
It looks for fresh angles.
Yellow loves new ideas.
Yellow is modern; it has the latest.
Yellow has no hesitation.
It decides quickly, and quickly acts.
Yellow does not suffer fools gladly.
Yellow smartens the reflexes.
Yellow is the great communicator.
It has no shortage of words.
Yellow is the journalist.
Yellow is the unifier.
It connects.
One of yellow's favourite pastimes is networking.
whether on a jungle drum or the telephone.
When something is revealed to yellow,
it immediately thinks of editing it
for the public rather than
feeling it for
itself.
Gossip is yellow.
The physical level of yellow communication is
the media – press, radio, TV,

entertainment.
The quiz master and the whizz kid are yellow.
On a higher level the yellow mode is telepathy.
Yellow is mental intuition.
Yellow is the orator.
Yellow goes to battle
in the name of justice and the law,
but with words and intellect, not the red sword.
The negative yellow of this trait appears in
the gangster and criminal.
Yellow is the censor.
Yellow can become a mental dictator.
Negative yellow is the fanatic who believes he has a
mission to do or set right regardless.
Hitler was the 20th century's
dreadful example of this aspect of negative yellow.
Negative yellow can be a coward.
Yellow is the executive level of business.
It is the ability to get things done.
Yellow is diplomatic.
It has self-control, style and sophistication.
Yellow likes to be well known.
Yellow loves admiration as much as red and orange.
It is just more subtle – the pen is mightier than the sword.
Furthermore, those who use the pen live longer –
and yellow is *very* interested in longevity.
Yellow can misuse words cleverly.
Instead of being an instrument of perception,
words then generate a fog of evasion.
Yellow does not like being cornered.
It responds to pressure
with evasiveness.
Yellow can be the first to

see and the last to
understand.
Yellow has the ability to make money,
usually by mental talent.
Keeping it may be more difficult.
Yellow thinks big when it comes to money.
Yellow despises pettiness.
Yellow is broadminded.
Yellow has no boundaries – just the same as love.
Yellow is freedom and joy, laughter and fun.
Yellow intends to keep its sunny side up.
Yellow's emphasis on reason can make it seem lacking in
compassion, even callous.
The antidote is to allow intuition to
override the head.
Yellow separates the human from the animal.
Yellow invented the fence.
This penned in the animals so that
they no longer had to be tracked down in
the forest.
So yellow discovered domestication,
which is the cornerstone
of civilisation.
Yellow is not fat – it keeps you in trim.
Yellow is so quick that excess
has no time to gather.
Yellow is sunny and willing –
unless upset, when it can become
acid and sharp-tongued.
Yellow is
connected to the seat of
self-confidence and self-esteem in the body.
Butterflies in the stomach are yellow.

'Am I good enough? Will they like me?'
are yellow questions.
Yellow is not good at pacing itself;
one thing leads to another.
Yellow finds it difficult to rest,
which makes it prone to nervous strain and breakdown.
Overuse of the intellect can lead
to mental collapse.
Yellow resists recognising physical limitation.
Chronic fatigue and lethargy are common
complaints of yellow.
Yellow's inability to stop can lead either to the stars –
or to death by sheer exhaustion.
Yellow
needs to get its priorities right.
Sacrificing sense for cleverness means you get neither.
Yellow does not like pie-in-the-sky thinking.
It prefers reality.
Yellow is: 'as you think, so you become'.
It knows that one's own mind
is the master of life.
Yellow always broadcasts a feeling of well-being.
People feel good around those under the
yellow ray ... which is exactly what
the yellow ray people
would wish.

THE MANY MOODS OF YELLOW
Shades and Tints

Dark Yellow: low self-worth; misplaced confidence
◆ Dark yellow is a vandal, crafty, treacherous and argumentative.
◆ This colour exemplifies the truth of: you can fester in the mind just as you can in the body.
◆ Dark yellow loves to set off rumours.
◆ Dark yellow is the deceiver.
◆ It is very cynical, regarding honour as stupidity.
◆ Those under its influence always expect the worst of others, and themselves – and are rarely disappointed.
◆ When these traits deteriorate even further, we enter the realm of the darker mustard yellow shades.
◆ Dark yellow is also extremely analytical – the yellow ability to think gone wild.
◆ It is also nagging, complaining and caustic.
◆ It can be mentally deficient.
◆ Eating disorders are connected to this colour.
Good example: Richard III.
Problems: Life's all a problem; joylessness.

Yellow Red – rashness; mercy
◆ The red in this colour creates rashness and impetuosity.
◆ The justice of yellow may turn into a harsh justice. Then the punishment far outweighs the crime. Transportation to the colonies for stealing a loaf of bread, for instance, is yellow red.
◆ The father who cuts the daughter off without a penny.
◆ This colour is the liquidator.
◆ Organised crime comes under this shade.
◆ Yellow red has the saving factor of purging, and also the

wonderful healing power of unexpected mercy.

Good examples: The hunter; the iron hand..

Problems: Rigidity; insane authoritarianism.

Lemon Yellow – practical

◆ The lemon yellow statement is: 'No one can pull the wool over my eyes.'

◆ This can get those under its influence a reputation for being critical and suspicious.

◆ Lemon yellow's comments can sting. On the other hand, its astuteness can be an asset.

◆ The good thing about lemon yellows is that they cut through the verbiage and red tape.

◆ They have to say what is – which is not always the most popular line.

◆ Their disposition can be a bit sour.

Good examples: Margaret Thatcher; the Trade Unionist's motto: 'One out, all out.'

Problems: Can appear uncaring; the misfit.

Citrine Yellow – fickleness

◆ Citrine yellow's emotions will be unstable, and often conflicting.

◆ If under too much pressure, citrine yellows are inclined to run away from responsibilities.

◆ Those under this hue must watch out for deceitfulness, both in regard to themselves and others. The citrine character can be a bit abrasive.

◆ Animosity is a trait of citrine. It will harbour past grudges.

◆ It can be foolish about money. It probably gave rise to the proverb: A fool and his money are soon parted.

◆ But citrines are discriminating, whose positive aspect is fairness.

◆ This colour can be a tease.

Good example: The coquette.

Problems: Animosity towards others; the malingerer.

Primrose Yellow – hyper-spirituality

◆ Though this colour is associated with great spirituality, it can be an erratic devotion.

◆ Unreliable is a primrose yellow word.

◆ It likes others to take over so it can step aside.

◆ Primrose yellow likes to opt out so that it can spend its time pursuing the unanswerable question: questioning loops that get you nowhere. When the answer to the question, 'Who made me?' is given as, 'God,' this colour comes back with, 'Mummy, who made God?'

◆ A positive aspect: this colour stretches one's mind, inciting it to question a world beyond the obvious. Pale yellow likes to search for an understanding into what is happening.

◆ Primrose yellow's gift to the intellectual world is the gifted child.

Good examples: The well-intended prophet; St Bernadette of Lourdes; Shirley Temple.

Problems: Getting nowhere fast; the false guru; the LSD trip.

> **'Thinking is the talking of the soul with itself.'**
>
> Plato

gold

'Silence from some is worth more than gold from others.'
Charlton Heston in *The Ten Commandments*

gold polarity
Trust – deception

positive gold keywords
Generosity; experience; maturity; wisdom; vitality; endless
supply; future; forgiveness; triumphant; access.

negative gold keywords
Suspicion; paranoia; crabbedness; limitation; pessimistic;
misfit; under-achiever; disgrace; conceit.

Gold is purity.
Gold does not seek, it has already found.
Gold expands the power of love.
Gold is glorious.
Gold represents the ultimate victory.
It transforms from victim to victorious.
Gold is the benefactor.
Gold is extremely gracious.
Gold asks that we trust and dare.
Gold's gift is released by trust.
When you trust you can surrender.
And when you surrender,
you can receive.
Gold has no victims, nor does it victimise.
Gold comes through.
It comes up trumps whatever the odds.

Gold gives access.
It gives entry to the unobtainable.
Gold is well-heeled.
Gold has always been
associated with money and material wealth.
Gold indicates treasure, the chest of golden coins,
the pawnbroker's three gold balls.
But gold has a higher meaning: gold
is soul experience.
The gold that
we pluck from the earth
is crystallised
sunlight.
Gold has experience from all that's past.
Gold has access to knowledge,
and – most important – to knowledge of the self.
Gold is purely itself.
Parasites are unable to hang onto it.
The saint's golden halo signifies that he has
become spiritually mature.
Gold is wisdom.
Gold can pass on wisdom.
It knows wisdom is given to be handed on to
others, not to be hoarded
for oneself.
Gold is nobody's fool,
or, as Gordon Gekko puts it in the movie, *Wall Street*:
'A fool and his money are lucky to get together
in the first place.'
Gold absorbs facts quickly.
It is the wise counsellor.
Gold is the rain of giving.
Negative gold is the drought of hoarding.

Gold is forgiveness.
The past wrongs we hoard and do not forgive
continue to happen to us.
Forgiveness means letting yourself off the hook.
The martyr's golden halo signifies that he
has moved beyond his trials.
Gold is an old colour, the colour of experience.
Gold is
the colour of autumn.
The young bud does not fall off the tree.
It has to experience the seasons first.
It is letting go of the past out of a
deeper understanding.
Gold is the colour of old memory.
Gold means that one has paid one's dues.
Gold radiates vitality and abundance for all.
Gold knows that there is an endless supply.
Whatever seems to have been lost
or taken away
will return.
Gold is the colour of Easter and resurrection.
Gold's beauty wins against all odds.
When lovers glow with the confidence of their love,
the aspect of gold is strong within them.
Gold eventually brings joy and happiness.
It is the sign of completion.
'And they lived happily ever after,'
is a golden ending ...
and beginning.
Gold does not require belief.
When one is working centred in gold, one just knows.
'I don't have to believe, I just know',
Carl Jung on being asked about his belief in God.

Gold is the sign of achievement
in the realms of
wisdom and understanding.
Victors can bask in the glory of gold.
The leader
always has a golden streak.
There is a depth of self-knowledge in the
leader that puts him
in front.
The humility of a child
and the wisdom of a true king unite
in the power of gold.
Gold is us following our leader in the trust that
he or she will lead us to liberation.
Gold not only has wisdom,
it knows how to put wisdom into action as well.
Gold knows what is needed in life.
It has a need to share this
knowledge with
mankind.
Gold believes in the unification of all nations.
It also believes in inherited wealth.
Gold finds the solution that yellow was looking for.
Gold in its negativity trusts no one.
This indicates an original mistrust of mother.
Negative gold has a fear of success,
a fear of failure,
a fear of being here at all.
Negative gold has unreal expectations –
fool's gold.
'All that glistens is not gold'
– old Spanish proverb.
Negative gold will blow its own trumpet.

Yellow's conceit is trivial compared to that of negative gold.
Gold's conceit is that of privilege and belief in one
being inherently more worthy.
It is quietly convinced of its own superiority.
Gold is the aristocrat of the conceits.
True gold is honour among men.
The colours in the rainbow's arch lead
from gold to gold.
Gold means: *'I am.'*
Unearth the gold within that can enrich you.
Gold signifies that which is outside of time.
Gold is immortality.
If you can't take it with you,
it may be because it's
already there!

There are no shades or tints of gold

'From whom are you to allow liberation?
None other but from your own mind (by) correct
knowledge and perfect understanding.'

His Holiness Param Sant

green

'The force that through the green fuse drives the flower
Drives my green age'
Dylan Thomas

green polarity
Balance – imbalance

positive green keywords
Discriminating; tactful; practical; stable; productive;
generous; highly imaginative; progressive;
reformer; unbiased; relationships.

negative green keywords
Jealous; resentful; forgetful; selfish; greedy; unimaginative;
unsettled; frustration; hypochondriac; scarcity.

Green is the heart centre.
Green is balance and harmony.
Green stabilises.
Green is the colour of the heart chakra.
The ability to experience wholeness;
love.
Green is agreeable.
Green is the bridge.
It is the gateway in the spectrum –
as the heart is in the body.
The lesson of love needs
to be learned in order to cross green's bridge.
Green centralises.
Green connects the flower above

with the roots below.
Green makes progress.
It is dependable.
Green restores.
Green is nature's wheel of unity.
Green is diplomatic and tactful.
Green is midway
between the hot magnetic colours of
red, orange and yellow
and the cooler electrical colours
of blue, indigo and purple.
Green is the bonder of the spectrum.
It bonds the magnetic red side with the
electrical blue side.
Green is a sanctuary, the halfway house of the spectrum.
Green likes partnership; it is always matchmaking.
Green is neither hot nor cold, active nor passive,
acid nor alkaline.
Green can discriminate.
Green compares.
It can see both sides ...
which gives it a tendency to moralise.
Green can make the right judgement.
It has the ability to weigh things up
and purge that which
must go.
Green can put itself on a moral pedestal,
particularly when the subject is the environment.
Green when negative would rather be admired than loved.
Green wants to take its proper place in life.
It wants to be acknowledged
for being who it is.
Negative green believes it can only be loved for what it does.

Green is clarity and understanding.
It helps one do the
best one can.
Green will encourage.
Green loves harmony and balance.
It achieves this through struggle and conflict.
Green represents the ups and downs of life.
Green is the practical philosopher.
It has great common sense by reasoning.
It tunes itself into nature.
Green contemplates.
Green is the reformer.
It makes changes.
Green does not just follow rules,
it creates better ones when the old have failed.
Green can get control of itself because of
its power to stabilise.
Its ability to re-establish balance restores
ease to the system.
Green strives
to keep a balance between
the mental interests of the head
and the emotional concerns of the heart.
Green gets to the core of the matter.
Green is very conscientious.
Green gives encouragement.
Green can indicate difficulty in finding a settled way of life.
There can be a conflict of ideas and emotions
that causes commotion
and upheaval.
But, with green's ability to discriminate and balance,
this conflict can lead to correct
judgement and action.

Green holds the key to memory – it can remember
that which it needs to know.
It unlocks the deep and hidden
that is the cause of our physical
and psychological
illnesses.
Green is an emotional indicator.
If a balance of green is not attained,
it can lead to pains of the heart: envy,
jealousy, and heart attacks.
A little green envy can act as a driving
force to achieve the same as others.
A little negative green can be
extremely positive –
sometimes.
Green is prosperous, particularly in business.
Green likes the 'good life'.
It wants the best.
Green knows the value of money.
It is the colour of finance and material wealth,
and of the economist.
Green is interested in property and real estate.
Green loves to collect possessions.
But positive green is the giver.
It is generous and loves to share what it accumulates.
Green is the great host.
Green represents the planet Earth
in its green mantle.
Green must have room to move, to expand.
'Give me space,' it says, 'Give me a green field!
I want to hug a tree.
Move out of my way, I need to breathe!'
Green opens doors.

Green is an idealist.
It has a social conscience,
but is a practical idealist.
It often helps others, even when this
is at its own expense.
Doctors are on the green ray.
Green loves children, animals, nature.
It represents new beginnings.
Green people love their home –
when you visit you get a great welcome.
Negative green is the colour of coping,
unquestioning acceptance and hopelessness;
of self-denial and self-suppression;
of a refusal to live fully.
Green's need for recognition can lead
to ulcers when frustrated.
Green is awareness of oneself.
It can show a desire to increase assertiveness.
Green is youth and growth.
Green – the improver for all – brings comfort
into the world.
A new awareness of green may indicate
that you are now prepared to
take your rightful place
in the world.

THE MANY MOODS OF GREEN
The Shades and Tints

Dark green – resentment
◆ Dark green is always on the defensive.
◆ Dark green suffers from extreme possessiveness, greed,
envy and jealousy.

- It can become blind to another's needs, wishes and emotions and believe that everything revolves around it.
- The tax system comes under dark green. Originally, tax was an imposition by the rich and powerful on the poor and weak. Robin Hood (red) had it right!
- Dark green needs to break away and create a life of its own.
- Someone under the influence of this vibration gives his or her power to other people.
- The darker the shade of green, the longer the struggle has been going on. It can show that the person is full of remorse.
- Someone under the influence of this colour can be unreliable.

Good examples: The narcissist; 'I'm all right, Jack'; the miser.
Problem: Never learning to say 'No'.

Emerald Green – charity; tolerance; adaptability

- The ray of great healers and healing.
- It is connected to great wealth – material as well as in ideas.
- Emerald green harmonises, and desires of the heart are gained.
- Heartfelt choices succeed without struggle.
- Emerald green has the key to unlock your heart.
- Emerald green gives in easily.
- Emerald green's magic makes you feel that it's good to be alive.

Good example: Your favourite grandfather or teacher.
Problems: Don't give a monkey's; nobody's at home; get lost.

Olive Green – treachery

- Olive green is made up of green and grey.
- It deceives, but it deceives no one but itself.
- Animosity is the other pitfall; an envy of anyone more advanced than itself.

◆ If someone was drawn to this colour, I would look for the areas in their lives where they were not being honest with themselves. Unfortunately, the person will truly believe that they are totally honest with themselves.

◆ Olive green has no imagination.

◆ Olive green refuses to recognise a disastrous relationship.

Good example: The underling.

Problems: It's always somebody else's fault.

Green/Gold – supply

◆ Green with gold in it becomes the supplier.

◆ It produces whatever is needed.

◆ The 'can get' personality, the one who has the connections, who comes up with the goods.

◆ The negative of this is the person who wants but never gets.

Good examples: The black marketeer; the buyer for a big store.

Problems: Not asking for what you want; always the bridesmaid.

Green/Blue – confidentiality

◆ This is the colour of someone who can be trusted with your deepest secrets. They have the ability to keep quiet about another's affairs.

◆ Green/blue has compassion and understanding for others, yet it is never one of the crowd.

◆ It does not get attached to its own generation.

◆ It is the scoutmaster who gives his life in the service of his troop.

◆ If drawn to this colour, you may be facing some important decisions in affairs of the heart.

◆ The negative is the blabbermouth.

Good examples: The confidant; the priest in confession.

Problems: Two-facedness; loneliness.

Pale Green – beginnings; immaturity

'My salad days / When I was green in judgement...'

Antony and Cleopatra, Shakespeare

◆ Pale green is tender, the new shoot, the learning time.

◆ Pale green is a fresh start, thus its connection with early childhood (birth to seven years).

◆ It is the development of the will. Thus the person with the 'Should I? Shouldn't I?' syndrome. An inability to make up one's mind.

◆ An adult drawn to pale green can be indicating childhood deprivation.

◆ Pale green can show sympathy and compassion. It encourages others to begin again.

◆ The negative of pale green is drought; nothing grows. It can show someone who starts things up but never finishes them.

◆ Also mutton done up like lamb – not willing to be one's age.

Good example: Peter Pan.

Problems: Not taking responsibility; immature.

Silver Green – misty

◆ Silver green is the time prior to conception.

◆ The silver reflects and the green is young, thus its wonderful utility in past life regression work.

◆ Even in past life work, silver green will go to the youthful time of that life rather than the heavy dramas of the incarnation. I use it when I want the lives that were *not* traumatic to come up. This way, I get to see the essence that keeps recurring, life after life – the sailor followed by the swimmer followed by the water engineer ... all connected through water.

◆ Silver green shows me what a person could have been; I look at the 'could-have-beens' in order to see what the person can be.

◆ This colour has a connection to definiteness of money: you either have it or you don't.

Good examples: The play, *Blithe Spirit*; the spiritual channel.

Problems: Wallowing in the past; the snobbery of class distinction.

Jade Green – worldly wisdom

◆ Jade green is the true giving of self from the heart. When I give a piece of jade to someone, I am trusting them with a piece of myself without expecting anything in return.

◆ It gives space for psychic knowledge.

◆ Negative jade looks for the hidden motive; it cannot trust the purity of just giving.

Good example: The Unknown Soldier.

Problems: Over-giving; imbalanced.

> *'He makes me lie down in green pastures,*
> *and leads me beside the waters of peace ...'*
>
> Psalms XXII, 2

turquoise

'Me, me, me, myself and I'

Anonymous

turquoise polarity

Self-Confidence – narcissism

positive turquoise keywords

Calmness; self-questioning; self-sufficient; personal; balance; harmony; success.

negative turquoise keywords

Reticent; fence-sitting; unreliable; boastfulness; deception; off-handed.

Turquoise looks to itself first.
Turquoise is single-minded.
Turquoise is emotional control.
Through the stillness of turquoise comes a deep peace.
It is nature's great natural tranquilliser.
Turquoise is the colour of balance.
Turquoise calms the nerves of the public speaker.
It feeds the central nervous system.
Turquoise is
the opener of the heart
and the healer of the emotions.
It penetrates into depths of feelings.
However, turquoise can be unaware of
its own heart's desires.
Turquoise's basic motivation in life is
emotional relationship.

It can also be a sexual two-timer because of its
refusal to decide which is the one.
Turquoise loves good friendship.
Turquoise aims to be a success.
It needs to make its own way in the world.
Turquoise has a need to be popular.
It likes to enjoy life.
Turquoise has a longing to know about life.
Turquoise has the gift of being able to see
who is going to win. It is very perceptive,
not through prophetic powers but out of an
ability to weigh up the odds.
Turquoise has a discriminating eye –
useful in antique dealings.
Turquoise can be extremely decisive.
It is good in an
emergency.
Turquoise says what it feels rather than
what is appropriate.
Turquoise is often asked to be the arbitrator.
It likes to get things settled.
Turquoise is the only colour that says:
'Stand still! What do I think?
What do I feel? What do I need?
Me, me, me!
Not mama, papa, the kids,
the cat and the universe,
but myself!'
Turquoise is a very human colour.
It loves sharing and togetherness, being together
and having a family.
Negative turquoise can be deceived about itself.
It can be over-emotional.

Turquoise can be an emotional manipulator.
Turquoise quite often has problems with affairs of the heart.
Extreme turquoise will be the narcissist.
The turquoise need to be popular can
lead to some boastfulness
and deception.
Turquoise is afraid of being alone. It hates being single.
In friendship, negative turquoise can
become cold and stand-offish.
Turquoise can be very lonely.
Turquoise can
find itself sitting on the fence
through trying to fix it so that everyone is happy.
But when turquoise gets down off the fence,
looks to its own wants and needs,
and makes a stand, it sticks
to its guns, come what may.
Turquoise is the beginning of ambition for the self.
Turquoise has an affinity with animals.

There are no shades or tints of turquoise

'Please hear what I am not saying.'
Charles C. Finn

blue

'We are all here on earth to help others.
What I can't figure out is what the others are here for.'
W.H.Auden

blue polarity
Knowledge – ignorance

positive blue keywords
Wisdom; patience; truth; mental attainment;
spiritual; philosophical; contemplative; quiet;
healer; integrity; loyal.

negative blue keywords
Weak; emotionally unstable; spiteful; superstitious;
intellectual conceit; sentimental love; frigid;
deceitful; unforgiving.

Blue is the spirit of truth.
Blue is the higher order of intelligence.
Blue is the colour of the throat chakra.
The ability to speak the truth and be heard;
self-expression.
It communicates by the voice.
Blue is the word.
Blue has a healing voice.
Blue can show you that you need to speak up for yourself.
Blue is the connection between
the body and the head.
The head and the heart speak through
the blue throat.

Blue listens closely to what you say –
and plays it back to you.
Blue reasons things out slowly and with integrity.
Blue is the teacher.
Blue is the colour of truth,
or, as Mark Twain put it: 'You can't pray a lie.'
Blue is peace with a purpose.
Blue has to be careful that it isn't peace at any price.
Blue will not draw attention to itself.
Blue doesn't like to sell, especially not itself.
Compared to the reds and oranges, blue is quiet.
Blue brings rest.
It cools and calms.
It slows down, and even retards growth.
Blue is the tranquil spirit.
It is the colour of contemplation.
Blue has higher philosophical thoughts.
It is the cosmic philosopher-scientist.
It looks towards the higher self.
Blue's thinking is quiet, discriminating and deep.
'Still waters run deep', is a blue motto.
Blue can be reticent.
But, like the sky, it is always there.
Blue values intellectual integrity.
Great writers are born
with the energy of the blue ray.
Blue works in a discreet and tactful way.
It prefers to maintain the status quo.
Ambassadors are blue.
Blue does not like upsets, yet often causes them.
Blue is family roots.
It takes one back to rituals that
marked out the family's identity.

Negative blue can show there was a lack of values
in the family.
Blue does things with honour and sincerity,
but its lofty ideals can make it rather aloof and remote.
Blue is highly inventive
in the realms of science and the arts.
Blue has the discrimination of wisdom, and
the wisdom of discrimination.
Blue is versatile and recognises that there
is something to be learnt in everything.
It penetrates to the soul.
Blue's wisdom is the antidote for an imagination run wild.
Blue has a poised quality.
It achieves this by constant struggle with its
susceptibility to mood swings.
Blue is a spiritual sedative.
Blue is particularly apt in counter-balancing fears of
'The end of the world is nigh' variety.
Blue has the ability to sober one up.
Blue brings a wisdom into love.
Blue doesn't always go by the book,
and even when it does, it will do so for only
so long as it suits blue's purposes.
Although honesty is a blue keyword, blue
also has a fear of honesty.
Honesty often requires confrontation and commotion,
both of which blue abhors.
Blue is a master of manipulation,
so good that you may not even know
you have been
manipulated!
Blue can be loyal, if it chooses.
Blue *will* do things its own way.

Blue longs for a change,
usually a change of its situation.
Blue looks before it leaps, but it *does* leap.
All the religions use blue as one
of their dominant
emblematic
colours.
Blue is as safe as heaven.
Blue can indicate that the person
is not happy in their present
circumstances.
Negative blue can be very separate,
snobbish and cold.
Blue can be frigid and spiteful.
Blue can show a moody and unforgiving
temperament.
Blue's diplomacy can be deceit using nice words.
Blue can be 'smother-love'.
Blue can get stuck in a rut.
Negative blue can have difficulty concentrating.
When blue becomes emotionally upset,
it is liable to let things slide.
It becomes the victim, the doormat.
Negative blue is the martyr syndrome:
'I am going to punish myself in order to
make you suffer.'
Blue is the seeker into all aspects.
Blue has an acceptance of that which
cannot be changed.
It makes the best of what is.
Blue has a great belief that it all turns
out right in the end.

And so blue can go
with the flow.
The Bible says: 'And the truth shall set you free.'
Blue uncovers the truth.

THE MANY MOODS OF BLUE
The Shades and Tints

Sky Blue – selfless love
◆ Sky blue is the universal healer.
◆ Sky blue remains calm and can overcome all obstacles.
◆ But, just like the sky, this colour is changeable, but constant.
◆ The blue sky will return if you wait long enough.
Good example: Monarchy.
Problem: Fear of not continuing.

Azure Blue – ambition
◆ Azure blue reaches for the stars, for high spiritual attainment.
◆ This rich blue colour has finished the waiting period.
◆ It can release a person from bondage.
◆ Those under its influence have found what they want and are going all out for it.
Good example: The Oxford-Cambridge boat race.
Problem: Missing the boat.

Pale Blue: inspires
◆ Pale blue uplifts.
◆ It is the soul searching for its maturity.
◆ It is a guide for the guides, it cares for the carers.
◆ It has constant faith and has the purity of innocence about it.

◆ It has a lovely lulling quality; it tones down the harsh and abrupt.
◆ Pale blue gives great encouragement to break loose from one's chains.
◆ Pale blue is constantly struggling towards a purpose.
◆ It can spark off the beginning of ambition.
◆ Pale blue can show that there is not much depth to the character – tries hard but doesn't succeed easily.
◆ Pale blue can do a great deal of work without much to show for it.

Good example: The free spirit.

Problems: Ignoring; turning the back on opportunity.

Dark Blue – single-mindedness
◆ The black in this blue indicates a restriction and a hardness.
◆ Dark blue is inclined to give justice without mercy. This can show up as a single-mindedness, whether for good or not-so-good ends.
◆ It can be a rather gloomy disposition.
◆ Dark blue is the worrier.
◆ It is someone dissatisfied with their lot.
◆ This colour can also indicate locked-up emotions.
◆ It can give the cold shoulder.
◆ Dark blue can be the bigot.
◆ Blue has clairvoyant ability; but in the dark blue it can be the charlatan.

Good examples: The pessimist; the misery.

Problem: Nothing is going to work.

'Truth, sir, is a cow.'
Samuel Johnson

indigo

'She would rather light candles than curse the darkness.'
Adlai Stevenson on Eleanor Roosevelt

indigo polarity
Devotion – blind faith

positive indigo keywords:
Perception; structure; regulations; idealism; fortitude;
purging; unflinching; obedience.

negative indigo keywords:
Fanatical; fascist; conformity; ritualistic; self-righteous;
liar; addiction.

Indigo has force and power.
It transmutes and purifies.
Indigo is the third eye, the brow chakra,
the ability to plan for the future.
Indigo can see more than is seen.
Indigo has a devotion to truth.
It unravels the unknown.
Indigo strives for the future.
It says 'I am going to do it' instead of just thinking about it.
Indigo is purity of thought.
Indigo is the transformer.
Indigo is the priest.
As a duck to water, indigo to reverence.
Indigo raises rules into holy rites.
The Commons raised to the House of Lords.
If blue avoids argument and row,

indigo has raised and refined this tendency to an
absolute belief in the pre-eminence
of the hierarchy.
Terror for indigo is no structure.
'I am structure' is indigo's identity.
Indigo is the third-eye opener.
Indigo's third-eye sight allows it to see
through the material world, but
leaves it lost
in space.
To anchor itself, it devotes its
energies to maintaining
ancient ways.
Indigo creates structures in which no deviation
or difference is considered either
possible or desirable.
Structure is indigo's safety net.
Indigo pares down to the bone.
There is no in-between for indigo.
It is all or nothing.
Indigo has unshakeable beliefs.
Indigo upholds
the Establishment to the end.
And if it cannot find an establishment,
it will create one.
Indigo loves law and order.
It will defend people's rights.
Indigo is justice, judge and jury.
Creating law and order is like an aphrodisiac to indigo.
Indigo
is very conscious
of the rungs of the ladder.
To be out of step for indigo is a

fate worse than
death.
Indigo is extremely conscientious and reliable
in a crisis.
Indigo's
devotional aspect
combined with its reforming fervour
enables it to reconstruct organisations – religious
or otherwise.
Indigo must watch that its work does not become
its sole interest.
Indigo holds the fort.
Indigo must learn to let someone else hold the fort
for a while.
Indigo thinks its indispensable.
Look to indigo, it always comes up trumps.
It finds that loan or gets that signature.
It always springs to the rescue.
Indigo aspires to be the spiritual master.
Indigo is spiritual antiseptic.
Intuition begins with indigo,
the first step to higher knowledge.
Indigo is a very dramatic colour – the drama queen.
The acting profession comes under the indigo ray.
Like the priest, the actor must give himself up
in order to play out a role.
Indigo can be moody; it's
never middling.
The indigo temperament is up in the clouds one minute,
and down in the dumps the next.
Workwise it can have great enthusiasm for a project
one minute
and then drop it suddenly.

Indigo is the devoted servant.
Intellectual fervour
has partly replaced
indigo's religious fervour in our society.
The addiction to qualifications is the indigo give-away.
Indigo is hungry for the meaning of life.
Indigo is the inspired preacher and writer.
Indigo can reconcile science and religion.
Its third-eye allows it to see the
true cause behind effect.
You will have to work with your indigo to understand this!
Indigo keeps telling you to pray,
but it doesn't tell you what is going to happen
when you do pray!
Indigo knows when to move energy
and when to hold fast.
Indigo constantly
pushes you into reviewing
your thinking.
Indigo gathers together, and makes whole,
so that the journey towards
'somewhere else'
can begin.
Indigo moves us on.
Indigo prepares for the realm of mysteries and
psychic dimensions.
Indigo personalities
can be dramatic and intoxicating.
On the sexual level, it can be the Don Juan
or the *femme fatale*.
Indigo can make incredibly sweeping statements.
Indigo *knows*.
Furthermore, you know they know ...

and they know you know they know that you know ...
Negative indigo can be low on trust.
Negative indigo has to be aware of self-deception
and a desire to show off which could make it unpopular.
Indigo's love of ritual can translate into addiction.
Rituals are a preparation for our intent;
unfortunately, we tend to forget what
our intention was.
Rituals are not the path.
They are a reminder that there is a path.
Blind devotion is an indigo failing.
Negative indigo can show a disturbing lack of purpose,
a belief in bad luck.
Just as indigo can see what cannot be seen,
it can also be blind to what is obvious.
Blinkered is the word.
Indigo without both eyes open can
become the fanatic.
Misplaced faith is the great weakness of indigo.
Negative indigo is the bigot.
Deep, dark indigo has a total lack
of understanding.
All addictions relate to negative indigo.
Addiction says:
'There is something wrong with the structure of your life.'
The desire for drugs
shows a desire for access to
indigo's powers of perception.
Unfortunately, the knowledge gained
through drugs will usually be
unable to be brought back.
Indigo's devotion is of the order:
'Even though thou slay me, I will not doubt thee.'

Indigo represents
an ocean of darkness.
But nonetheless it beckons us to cross.
Indigo is the threshold to other spheres.

There are no shades or tints of indigo.

*'Though I disapprove of what you say, I will defend
to the death your right to say it.'*

Voltaire

purple

'Man is a spiritual being who, in order to be truly spiritual, needs a body.'

St Thomas Aquinas

purple polarity
Peace – conflict

positive purple keywords
Rulership; selfless; dignity; humanitarian; inventive; orator; mentally creative; unlimited; psychic; mystic leader.

negative purple keywords
Ritualistic; ruthless; spiritual arrogance; pompous; corruption; social climber; delusions of grandeur.

Purple is the royal ray.
Purple is the ruler.
Purple is associated with the seventh chakra.
The ability to appreciate time in
all its dimensions.
Purple is the spiritual master.
Purple is the protector.
Purple is the spirit of mercy.
Purple is dignified.
Purple is visionary.
It works with the highest levels of thought.
Purple is the aristocracy of the spirit.
Purple is the highest note of the scale.
It is seeing and hearing without using
the physical senses.

'My words fly up, my thoughts remain below.'
Shakespeare's *Hamlet.*
Purple commands respect.
It strives for spiritual perfection.
Purple is people in high places.
Purple sees a richness with quality.
Purple uses its psychic perception on an everyday basis.
Purple comes to understand that the price it
must pay for its royal attributes
is sacrifice.
Purple has access to power. It has no limitations.
Purple has true greatness.
It can sacrifice itself for the benefit of all
without being a victim or martyr.
Purple came in with the Romans.
Only the emperor was allowed to wear purple robes.
Purple encourages you to become your own leader
and master.
Purple prefers to be self-employed.
Purple is found in the corridors of power.
Purple is always the leader of the pack.
Purple is always playing a leading role in the community.
Purple is highly inventive.
Purple is full of inspiration and originality.
Purple is the great teacher who realises
that the pupil has to understand.
Facts alone are not enough.
Purple is the humanitarian who has the wisdom of the king
and the humility of the child.
Purple's kindness is never mistaken for weakness.
Purple is poise and humility
Purple's motto is: 'Be ye as wise as serpents and as
harmless as doves,' *Matthew X, 16.*

The highest level of the purple ray
produces the great mystical leaders.
It is the colour of the psychic and pure spiritual qualities.
Purple's downfall is wanting
power for power's sake.
Purple desires perfection in all things.
Purple's lower levels can result in an inclination to
the black side and black magic.
Negative purple can show
a love of pomp and self-importance.
It can be insanely ruthless and corrupt.
In an emperor, this can result in a Nero.
Pride can rear its ugly head in negative purple.
Negative purple can be belligerent and treacherous.
Purple has a universal conscience.
It is the enlightened guru.
Purple is idealism.
The purple ray is that of the gifted poets, writers,
painters and musicians – the masters
in any creative field.
Purple is the peace-maker.
It combines power with gentleness.
Purple is self-assured.
It encourages others' self-esteem.
Purple makes your inner candle burn brighter.
Purple marches to the beat of a different drum.
It will not mix with the crowd.
Purple, being made of red and blue,
has the body of red and the spiritual nature of blue held in
perfect union.
Purple is the bridge to higher planes of consciousness –
the springboard to the infinite.
Purple is the heart of the universe in your hands.

THE MANY MOODS OF PURPLE
Shades and Tints

Deep purple – overbearing
◆ Because of the greater proportion of black in deep purple, it can use power corruptly.
◆ This colour can become dedicated to an ideal at the expense of human reality.
◆ Deep purple marries for position rather than love.
◆ Deep purple can be a ruthless seeker of power and very arrogant.
◆ It can also show a tendency towards suicide and deep depression.

Good examples: Dogmatism; the drug barons; tyrants.
Problem: Suppression of freedom.

Violet – spiritual service
◆ Violet adores to revere.
◆ It is very like purple, but not so intense.
◆ It is the rebuilder of ideals.
◆ It will sacrifice old ritual formats for the new, and even allows you to change religions.
◆ Violet likes to busy itself with occult and spiritual matters. It has spiritual dedication.
◆ Violet can yearn for emotional security and shy away from responsibility.
◆ As a friend, violet can be here one minute, gone the next, like a cream cake, naughty but nice.
◆ Violet is intuition, not intellect.
◆ Violet aids psychic ability.
◆ It can see into the future and seems to receive the divine nudge.
◆ Those under violet seem to have the knack of bridging time.

◆ Violet is good for use in regression to acknowledge your child from other times.
◆ Negative violet can flaunt its powers; it can be the misinformed mystic. Can lose its mind in this area. Cults built upon brainwashing techniques are in the negative violet.
◆ It does not adjust well to a decline in its circumstances.
◆ Violet is usually outstanding in its life work.
◆ Violet has a deep inner knowing of its destiny. Cinderella was working with violet.

Good examples: The selfless mystic; visionary.
Problem: Flowery and dramatic.

Amethyst – protector

◆ Amethyst links one with mystical powers. It is the spiritual ray which protects you while you reach out to the beyond.
◆ It is the great preparer for ceremonial magic.
◆ It enables you to see visions beyond the human eye.
◆ The monks were very conscious of its protective powers.
◆ It helps one pass through boundaries and to acknowledge karmic debts. Amethyst has both the crimson and the blue rays within it.
◆ Idealism is its key.
◆ It protects those who are unable to protect themselves – small children, the sick and vulnerable, and animals.
◆ Missionaries relate to this colour: the amethyst vibration sends them out to the unknown to guide and help mankind.
◆ Amethyst goes beyond the most calculated academic reasoning. It helps one assess who is sincere and who is not.
◆ Negative amethyst has no method at all and completely lacks mastership, often getting caught up with impractical ideals.

Good examples: Democracy; Statue of Liberty.
Problem: Impractical.

Mauve – aristocrat

◆ Mauve is majestic.
◆ Mauve can make right choices peacefully and calmly.
◆ The classic mauve type is the person who has been born the 'right side of the blanket'.
◆ It is the colour of dynasties.
◆ It is the state that the social climber imagines they will find when they reach their goal.
◆ Negative mauve believes that in some circles it is a serious blunder to use the wrong fork.

Good example: Lord Mountbatten.
Problem: Lack of etiquette; common.

Plum – full-blown

◆ Plum doesn't strive to attain anything. It already has it.
◆ It is the privileged who know they are so and take full advantage of it.
◆ Plum is old-fashioned.
◆ It is the name-dropper.
◆ Plum is in love with its own publicity.
◆ Plum is indulgent.
◆ In the spiritual field, it has false pride and a holier-than-thou attitude.
◆ Plum never talks to you. It gives a sermon. The personality is so earnest. Plum can be so pompous and boring.
◆ The plum personality is drawn to the land and livestock. It has an interest in good breeding.
◆ Positive plum can be the inspiring schoolteacher that the child never forgets.
◆ Plum's aim is to be established.

Good examples: Blue blood; family crests and tradition.
Problems: Impostors; ageing starlet.

Lavender – delicate

◆ Lavender is sensitive.
◆ Lavender is the lady in silk.
◆ Also elusive and fragile, lavender can be very evasive.
◆ Lavender is not always as delicate as it seems – the iron butterfly.
◆ Lavender is the love of beautiful things.
◆ Lavender attracts.

Good example: Exquisite porcelain beauty.
Problem: When the chips are down, lavender people disappear.

Lilac: self-appreciation.

◆ Lilac represents vanity, too much or too little. There is nothing wrong in looking in a mirror so long as it's not at every one you pass.
◆ Lilac loves glamour, romance and magic!
◆ It is immaturity, adolescence. Lilac is springtime.
◆ It is the colour that says, 'When I am grown up I am going to be...'

Good example: The adolescent girl.
Problems: Lilac can reveal a troubled childhood; growing up too soon.

> *'New faith means that we are confident of what we hope for, convinced of what we do not see.'*
>
> Hebrews II, 1, 2

grey

'Parting is such sweet sorrow.'
Romeo and Juliet, Shakespeare

grey polarity
Black – white

positive grey keywords
Informed; sanity; realism; linking; opposites;
respectable; stoicism.

negative grey keywords
Fear of losing; poverty; illness; criticism; melancholy;
sorrow; depression; austere.

Grey is the bridge between black and white.
Grey is the transitional stage.
Innocence and ignorance meet in grey,
thus grey's vulnerability.
These two traits were once considered essential and
most desirable in bringing up young ladies.
Unfortunately all they ever led to was disaster.
Grey feels it doesn't belong anywhere.
Grey is not wanted.
Grey is the colour of the Puritan epoch.
They were respectable people.
Grey is never first.
Children perceive grandparents as the colour grey.
Grey is as firm as a rock.
Grey strives for a harmonious stability.
Grey does not believe in emotional pain.

It likes to control emotional outbursts.
Grey believes emotions should be in their proper place,
But this is hardly ever right now!
Grey reveals stark reality and blocks deception.
It can stabilise the disturbed.
Dark grey can lead to loss of perspective
and bizarre behaviour.
The black and white of grey symbolises
the female/male.
Grey always seems to be split in two.
In ancient teachings the male
was thought to light up
the dark womb.
Grey is mainly attached to negativity.
People usually work on the negative of grey.
Negative grey is critical.
It fears its own lack of definition.
Grey is illness – it never feels well.
Negative grey is sadness and melancholy.
there is no future for grey.
It knows it's old, frail, and about to die.
Grey is always old; it knows no youth.
Old dry bones are grey.
Grey is a reminder to man of what he will become.
'Ashes to ashes, dust to dust.'
Grey puts a dampener on things.
Grey at its weakest
believes it cannot have it today.
It might get it tomorrow, but tomorrow never comes.
'There is never enough' is the negative grey statement.
The Victorian workhouse that punished
Oliver Twist for not having
poverty consciousness

was under the negative of the grey ray.
Grey at its best is optimistic,
and knows that the best is yet to come.
Grey, like steel, knows that it has to be tempered
before a new shape can emerge.
Grey has usually been knocked about a bit.
Grey must armour itself.
Our modern-day armour is the grey suit.
Grey is always out of date.
Positive grey – nothing is out of date if you love it.
Grey lends strength to someone who feels
inwardly weak and vulnerable.
Too much grey hardens.
Persistence and endurance are the grey aspects
of the life force, and will
eventually lead
to serenity.
The person drawn to grey can be
looking for the ideal emotional relationship.
Positive grey is the release from bondage.
People during the war were living
the negative of grey.
However, their belief
that they would come through
was working with the positive of grey.
Concentration camp survivors,
the hostages who 'knew they would make it',
were all working with the positive of grey.
Because grey is rock bottom, the only
way left to go is up!
Grey represents mouldiness and mildew,
but penicillin was discovered in a mould!
Grey symbolises transitions of all earthly things.

It leads our thoughts beyond destruction of all that's
material to the external.
Grey is divine in its destruction because rebirth can occur
and the flow continue.

THE MANY MOODS OF GREY
Shades and Tints

Light grey: salvation
◆ Light grey is a higher vibration of grey because it has more
white in it.
◆ It is the rescuer. Mother Teresa wore pale grey – this
showed she was working on the aspect of salvation.
◆ It is extremely soothing.
◆ It brings about great peace of mind and tranquillity.
◆ Pale grey is the beginning or end of a journey.
◆ Pale grey can feel it doesn't belong, it's not staying.
Good examples: Ghosts; visions.
Problems: Obscurity; unattached.

Dark grey: stricture; prison
◆ Dark grey is conventional to the point of narrow-
mindedness.
◆ It can produce unpleasant emotions.
◆ Dark grey is self-deception.
◆ It is the shade of suffering and poverty; and so of shame
and humiliation.
◆ Dark grey is austerity. There is a belief that there is never
going to be enough.
◆ It is the tortured mind, always trying to escape from some
unknown anxiety.
◆ 'Why hast thou forsaken me?' – Christ on the cross.
◆ Leprosy is the dark grey disease.

- Wretched, disgusting, sordid, derelict, are dark grey words.
- Dark grey is not wanted.
- The dark grey personality always manages to put a blemish on the proceedings.
- The person feels caged, trapped, that there is no way of escape, at the end of the line – the animals in the zoo.
- Dark grey is bizarre behaviour rather than clinical insanity – the person in the bed-sitting room with 40 dogs and 30 cats and old newspapers piled to the ceiling.
- The expression 'their wings are clipped' sums up the dark grey syndrome perfectly.

Good examples: The down-and-out-but-still-living; grandparents.

Problem: As an ex-inmate of Auschwitz put it: 'I think that God has gone on holiday.'

'All cats are grey in the night.'

Anonymous

silver

'Every cloud has a silver lining.'
Anonymous

silver polarity
Waxing – waning

positive silver keywords
Illuminates; reflects; unbiased; penetrating;
yearning; fluidity.

negative silver keywords
Two-faced; split; elusive; lunatic; crocodile tears; deceptive.

Silver illuminates.
Silver is the feminine.
Silver has the quality of endurance.
Silver stills the emotions.
It's the great natural tranquilliser.
Silver is flowing.
It is the fluid state of consciousness.
Silver always brings freedom from emotional restriction.
Still waters run deep.
Silver is the penetrator. It pierces.
Silver seeks money. It likes to have its palm crossed
with silver.
Silver yearns for spiritual harmony.
Silver restores equilibrium.
It solves disputes.
Silver is unbiased. It will allow you to have
your own opinion

without having a desire to change it.
The quicksilver mind pours out what is required.
Silver can be a bit slippery. It likes to move on.
The silvered mirror reflects.
It shows you as you are.
Silver is the movies.
Silver lays bare.
It does not cover up mistakes.
Silver illuminates; it lights up the path.
'By the light of the silvery moon ...'
When the moon is favourable the celestial conditions will
enable man to succeed in his efforts to transcend his mind.
It can show that a person is full of illusion
and living a life that doesn't exist.
Silver loves to fantasise.
Silver has always been connected with the moon,
the seat of astral glamour.
An invisible silver cord is said to attach
us to 'the other side'.
At death, the cord is severed from
our human body and
we move on.
Negative silver is schizophrenia,
or simply someone who is unable to make decisions.
Silver is at its most powerful at the full moon.
Negative silver shows up in relationships where there is
no substance, just delusion.
Negative silver is mutton done up as lamb.
Negative silver loves to wallow in emotion.
People who fall in love with stars of the
silver screen are under the negative of silver.
Silver is the thread of cosmic intelligence.
It governs the waxing and waning of life

through everything on
our planet –
the rise and fall of sap in trees,
the tides, the menstruation
of women.
The expression, 'I don't know whether
I am coming or going' is
working with this aspect of silver.

There are no shades or tints of silver

'Blue curtains of the sky, scatter thy silver dew
On every flower that shuts its sweet eyes
in timely sleep ...
And wash the dusk with silver.'
To the Evening Stars, William Blake

black

'The most beautiful thing we can experience is the mystery.'
Albert Einstein

'Any colour, so long as it's black.'
Henry Ford

black polarity
Fullness – emptiness

positive black keywords
Right use of power; creativity; instructor;
visionary ability; contained;
hidden riches.

negative black keywords
Destructive; power used out of weakness and selfishness;
dominance; depression; withholding;
restrictions.

Black contains and hides.
Black is visionary ability;
the seeing of that which is hidden.
Black is connected to higher philosophical
thoughts and ideals.
Black can be restricted and restricting.
One of the first questions
I ask myself when I see
someone dressed all in black is:
'What have they got bottled up inside them?'

Black
indicates that
something is lying dormant or buried.
The black of winter contains the
seeds for the next
spring.
Black is an end.
But out of black come all new beginnings.
Black is connected to mystery – the dark.
It points to magic and esoteric knowledge.
Black is the colour that holds
the power of judgement,
thus, the black robes of High Court judges.
Black is control,
not control by the physical dominance (red),
but by the occult.
Black does not want to give up anything
to keep control.
Black can show that a person has a need to be in control,
a state that is often caused by fear.
Nothing is as black as it seems.
Pure black is rare.
Black holds onto every colour within itself and
lets no colour escape.
Thus, it is the colour of the person who
keeps control by not giving
information to others.
Black makes you stand on your own.
Black is the absorber that gives nothing out.
The challenge for each of us in black is to bring our
true self out of the night.
Like breathing, this is a two-way process.
Every morning we

pull ourselves out of the dark
and go out into the world to do our day's work.
Every evening we return gratefully
for a night of restoring
sleep.
The black of night
holds the promise of rest
from the daily battle to survive.
We retreat within black to rest and
wake into the light again.
Black, in this aspect of withdrawal and retreat from the
glare of the day, from the publicity of the spotlight,
indicates an urgency to relinquish oneself,
one's identity and ego,
so that one can experience
the realm of purity.
'I want to be alone,' as Greta Garbo put it.
But you can only merge yourself with black safely
if you have selfless love,
thus the danger in black magic that is done for the
self only – in contrast to white magic
done for the good of all.
Nuns are working on the higher order of black when they
undertake to
relinquish their personality as
they embark upon a life of
worldly restriction and
hiddenness.
Black will renounce again and again and again.
There is nothing weak about black,
which is probably why it is feared.
Black is a promise.
It only becomes negative when depression sets in

because of disappointments in life.
Then we see everything
in a muddy light.
The devil is the epitome of negative black.
Remember that all that walks in the sun cast shadows.
Black is seductive.
The villain twirling his black moustache
has a subtle temptation.
In old black-and-white Westerns,
the baddie always wore
the black hat.
Black, when used for the wrong reasons, brings in
the worst aspect of the will and power:
harsh behaviour, treachery
and deceit.
Black used in the right way is the dark earth
out of which all new life springs.
But remember: a little black goes a long way.
Overdoing the black causes regression
instead of progression.
Black is the end –
and the beginning.
The day begins in the dark, and ends in the dark.
Our life begins in the unknown and
ends in the unknown.
Black is silent.
Death is silent.
But if we listen to silence we hear that this
silence has a sound.
Black's great challenge is to go beyond our fear of
losing our individual life in order to merge
into cosmic unity,
going into our personal dark to discover

the universal light.
Black brings us face-to-face with the
personal death that is the door to liberation.
This is black as the dark night of the soul
where all that is familiar
is swept away.
Depression is a black colour.
Negative black is the fear of what is next,
because black can be tragic mourning.
Black says: 'Do not seek death – it will find you.'
Death is an eternal opportunity.
The symphony of life swells up and down.
How about making the finale the best?
There is always something coming from the darkness,
whether it's the Christmas rose through
the sunless silence of winter
or a new-born babe from a
mother's dark womb.
Black reminds us that at the end is death, and the
pleasure of certainty.
Positive black is going forward to meet
the new with a light heart, regardless.
'Come to the edge,' he said.
They said, 'We are afraid.'
'Come to the edge,' he said.
They came. He pushed them and they flew.
Guillaume Apollinaire

There are no shades or tints of black

*'I died to the inorganic state and became
endowed with growth, and then I died to vegetable
growth and attained to the animal. I died from animality
and became Adam (Man):
Why then should I fear? When have I become less by dying?'*

The Persian Poet, Rumi

pearl

'Neither cast ye your pearls before swine.'

Matthew VII, 6

pearl polarity

Acceptance – rejection

positive pearl keywords

Lustre; soft; glowing; roundness;
perfection; strength; calm; multiple.

negative pearl keywords

Irritable; weakness; dull; uneven;
flawed; impenetrable.

Pearl is luxury.
Pearl gives strength and purifies the mind.
Pearl is culmination.
One can find every colour in pearl
if one looks long enough.
Pearl has a subtle warmth.
It responds to the warmth of the human skin.
Pearl is organic.
Pearl has an open-and-shut quality.
The pearl personality does not like to be intruded upon,
it has a habit of clamming up, like its cousins.
The hypersensitive person is under the
negative aspect of pearl,
also the recluse and hermit.
Pearl is the subtle mixer and merger.
Someone who refuses to answer may be

working with the negative of pearl.
Their mouth is shut
like an oyster.
The pearl personality
may seem remote and impenetrable – even dowdy.
But it is a case of the pearl in the grey shell.
Pearl is the unexpected achiever.
Pearl is balmy.
Pearls have a mysterious relationship with the moon.
An old remedy for keeping pearls
in perfect condition was to
bathe them in
moonlight.
An Indian belief is that pearls represent
solidified semen.

There are no shades or tints of pearl

'Full fathom five, my father lies;
Of his bones are coral made.
Those are pearls that were his eyes;
Nothing of him that doth fade ...'

The Tempest, Shakespeare

EXERCISES

Following are some practical exercises using the precise colour required for maximum emotional impact on the psyche, which encourages and promotes physical healing.

The Towel Technique – A Bright Red Anger Release

Repressed anger, anger that remains in the system, is like a can of worms with the lid kept on.

You may well ask why the anger shouldn't stay in. Do you tire easily? Is your energy used up quickly? If so, you may have repressed anger that needs to be released because it uses up a great deal of your energy to keep it down. High blood pressure and angina caused by a tired heart can come about because of repressed anger. You may say, 'But I don't feel angry at all!' But of course you won't feel it if it is deeply submerged.

Another aspect of anger is boredom, which is also related to the colour red. The bright red of anger is active, whereas the dull red of boredom is lethargic. The person who is bored is also tired and listless. Underneath boredom you will find there is repressed anger. When you take the lid off boredom it allows the bright red of anger to come to the surface. A good old anger release will work wonders. A simple process which will help to release this anger is the Towel Technique. This technique frees the energy so that it can be harnessed for the individual's benefit.

Wringing the towel is a very useful training action to help you learn how to feel angry. Often, when we were children, we were not able to express our anger or to experiment with it, or know that when it comes it can be released quickly to blow away. We were told, 'Don't be angry, it's not on.' We learned that this is an undesirable emotion, so we block it and repress it. We will always experience it but will not know what to do with it because we have not been trained to use it appropriately. The towel process allows you to practise with your anger and it's great fun. You can give yourself permission to be as angry as you like, for no other reason than just to feel anger. You will find it's not a taboo feeling. Appropriately used it is as important as all the other emotions, but you can't use it effectively unless you've had some practice – after all you wouldn't go on stage without rehearsing first.

THE TOWEL TECHNIQUE

1 First of all, find a hand towel, preferably red but any colour will do. Sit in a chair and make sure that you are really slouching so that your bottom is near the edge of the seat. Your legs should be apart and your back should be curved with your stomach concave.

2 Hold the towel at arms' length with your elbows straight. your hands should be about four inches apart. Do not curve your wrists underneath or around the towel. Keep the top of your hands facing up and only let the fingers curl round.

3 Now feel your feet securely placed on the ground and for a few moments just look at the space between your two hands, because you are going to wring the living daylights out of that space.

4 Now take a deep breath and hold it. Then bear down into your body so that you can feel a pressure in your lower abdomen and bowel area. It's a feeling of strain in the lower part of the body as though you are constipated and having to push hard to pass a motion. At the same time, wring that towel. If you want to you can let out a grunting sound as you breathe out.

5 If you don't feel angry, just fake it and you will find that sooner or later you will get immense action both physically and vocally doing this process. Try thinking of someone who upsets you and shout, scream or growl at them. Swear if you wish. It's much better to do it this way than to wring their neck!

This process takes only two-and-a-half minutes a day and you will start to release your repressed anger. This anger could have been there since birth and babyhood. Repressed anger will not allow your body to relax fully, so wring a towel and give your circulation a treat. Just one super wring is enough to change your body's energy. If you feel depressed, wring a towel and after just one breath it will start to spring you out of it and you'll begin to feel better immediately.

A Sun Shower for the Mind – A Yellow Visualisation

The mind is the composer of the body's activities. This is a colour cleansing exercise for the mind. It makes use of yellow's richness, the colour of the mind's mental processes. Like the Rainbow Tonic, you can use it anywhere and anytime.

This is a good exercise for those times when your mind is full of fears, of dark thoughts and black places. It is excellent for depression of any kind. When a person is sad they are full of feeling, but when they are depressed they are empty. I call depression a colour drain. I see it as a black rainbow – the dark, desperate side of the soul. The sunlight has gone behind the cloud but light can break through where no sun shines. This is why gold is the great healer for depression.

What is behind that cloud? Usually there is anger and sorrow. When a client visits me in deep depression, I am careful not to tell them to be positive. Obviously, a person in such a depressed state feels they have nothing to be positive about. What the person needs is tools to work with. I encourage a person in depression to go into that dark cave. What the person will usually find when they get in there is only what they took in with them, which is themselves.

The nature of depression is that the person tends to become very inert. But there is always a funny side, even for someone in depression. As one optimistic but depressed client once exclaimed to me, 'At least being a depressive you get your rest!'

The root of depression must be grasped, taken in hand. When the dark and hidden fear that is the heart of depression is in the person's hands it can be dissolved. Always wear colours if you are depressed. Light can enter and the dark rainbow be transformed into its spectrum of colours.

To escape the domination of the mind can be a Himalayan task. Part of the purpose of this exercise is to experience a mind bubbling with joy rather than irritation. By using it over a period of time, you will be able to have the joy-filled mind as your natural state. It is also a process that enables you to be receptive to the power of love and desire. It clears the mind of shadows. When the mind is shadowed and blocked, the power it has to have your desires fulfilled is also inhibited. Whatever your needs, the sun shower brings you closer to being able to allow the universe to meet them:

A SUN SHOWER FOR THE MIND

1 It is preferable to do this process lying down. Make yourself comfortable, close your eyes and begin a pattern of deep, slow breathing. See yourself inhaling long, slow breaths of goodness into your body and exhaling all negativity.

2 Now turn your thoughts to your mind. See it as a room.

Note what is in this room. Is the room cluttered up? Is there a colour to the clutter? Are there any grey or dark patches?

3 As you continue breathing gently and slowly, allow your mind to become very still and very quiet. You may actually feel it settling down. This may take a few minutes to happen – the mind sometimes resists slowing down because it is used to being busy. Be patient with your mind in this part of the process. Just be aware that you are letting go of all thoughts so that your mind can become still and very calm. It is like a liner coming up to the quayside after a long voyage. You may even feel a slight jolt when your mind finally comes to rest.

4 When you feel your mind has come to rest, imagine an opening appearing in the top of your head. A soft, warm, yellow ray of light is beaming down from an indigo sky above. It pours through the opening in the top of your head and streams into your mind's room bursting into a million sparkling gold stars.

5 Let this light fill the mind. Let it seep into every space and every corner. Fill your mind's room with this liquid sunlight.

As your mind fills with this lovely yellow light, it becomes buoyant and cheerful. Any black-spots or grey areas will be cleared as the light filters through them. And, as your mind becomes clearer, so your body becomes lighter and more joyous. You can stay in this state for as long as you wish.

6 When you decide to return, gently close the opening in your head. As you do, become aware of your breathing again. Take several deep breaths to bring you back into the world. Wait a few minutes before moving because you may experience a light-headedness. , shuffle feet

The Inner Child Process – Spring Green

This is a technique by which you can make acquaintance with your own little child, the child who lives within you. Though there are many other little child exercises, the effects of this one are so deep and moving that I would recommend that it be the first one used for inner child work.

When we grow up, we take over parenting our inner child from our parents. As we were parented so we parent our inner child. The inner child stays with us until the day we die; the child is who we are. I feel our child is within our abdomen; we carry it around with us.

The magic of cuddling our inner child is that we as parents can now give it anything it needs or wants. Thus, we can ourselves become whole and well again instead of victims and always incomplete. We cannot change the happenings of childhood, but we can certainly release any painful energies that remained with us.

I have found that people with whom I am doing this exercise will often cry with relief at the reunion with their lost child who has been wandering around for years, ignored and alone. The release can be so great that body changes appear – the person becomes softer, and a contentment enters their presence. So often people go around searching for something all their lives. What they do not realise is that what they are looking for is for the little child that they lost so long ago.

THE LITTLE CHILD PROCESS

1 Take one of your jackets and roll it up into a bundle. It is important to use one of your own.

2 Put the jacket bundle close at hand, and sit on a chair with

your feet firmly on the ground and the lower part of your back firmly supported by the chair.

3 Take the jacket in both hands and, keeping secure hold of it, place it on top of your knees.

4 Look upon the bundle and be very aware that you are now holding yourself as a small child.

5 You are now going to talk to this little one who has never heard from you before. When I use this process with a client, I tell the person to gaze upon their child and repeat the following words after me: 'I will never, ever leave you again.' Pause ... 'Not ever. You are always coming with me. Do you hear me?' Pause ... 'I will never, ever leave you behind again.' Pause ... 'Not ever. You are always coming with me.' Pause ... 'Always.'

6 Repeat this until you *know* your little child has heard it.

7 Finally, draw the little bundle into your arms. Hold it close against your chest and rock it gently.

You may need to repeat this process once a day for as long as it takes for your little child to understand fully. Remember, he or she has been living in a state of fear of being left behind, and has always been left behind. You as the adult were now will embrace your own inner child, so that it will never be alone again.

The Tumble Roll – The Violet-Orange Back-to-the-Womb Process

This process/exercise is to help you release any negative experiences you may have had while you were in the womb. The fact that you do not consciously remember these is not a problem – your body does and it would love to let them go.

You may, at first, find this a long and quite complicated process, so you may want to ask a friend to talk you through it. In fact, two people can take turns.

It is most important during the Tumble Roll exercise to be aware of your breathing. Keep breathing regularly all the way through it, and try not to stop. If you have a friend with you, ask them to remind you to keep breathing normally. You may find you want to breathe faster, or slower. If so, be aware of it and go back to your regular breathing.

Several things may happen during this exercise. You may have a rush of intense feelings, or you may find that you seem to go numb or blank. Crying, coughing, shaking, yawning deeply, even laughing at nothing at all, are releases of energy. Whatever form the release takes you can be sure that you are getting in touch with your birth trauma and that the experience you are having is perfectly appropriate. This process is using the power of colour to heal quickly and simply.

THE TUMBLE ROLL

1 Lie flat on the floor with your eyes closed. Your body and legs are relaxed, your arms lying loosely by your sides, your palms facing up to the ceiling. This is called the Dead Man's Pose.

2 Begin breathing deeply, consciously relaxing every part of your body. Begin at your feet and move up the body until you reach the top of your head. Imagine each part becoming heavier and heavier. This may take you some minutes, but it is an essential part of the process.

3 Having completed 2, visualise the air around you filled with the colour violet. You can use the Star-Breath Technique on page 117 for this.

4 After five minutes of breathing in violet, sit up. Keep your eyes closed and your back as straight as possible. Keep

breathing in the violet light. Next, bring your knees up to your chest. Cross your ankles (it doesn't matter which ankle you cross over which), and fold your arms around your knees, clasping them to your chest. You should now look like a little foetus curled up in the womb. Finally, let your head roll forwards and come to rest on your knees. Do this position as well as you can, but don't overstrain.

5 Imagine your arms holding your knees filling up with orange light. Some people find that being in the foetal position brings up fear and they immediately want to come out of the position. Traumas in the womb always put the foetus into fear, particularly of moving forward. The orange arms absorb shock and support you while you experience the process. If you experience feelings of fear coming up, just acknowledge them and say, 'Yes, I feel fearful' and then let them go.

6 In this position, start to rock backwards and forwards gently. Let yourself fall into a rhythm of slow rocking – backwards and forwards, backwards and forwards ... There can be a tendency to hold your breath at this stage, but keep breathing! And don't worry if you fall over. Just keep your eyes shut, sit up again and keep going.

7 After five minutes of this exercise, let your rocking gradually come to a halt, release your arms slowly and, still keeping your eyes shut, lie back on the floor again in the original Dead Man's Pose. As you do, let the orange that filled your arms drain away out through your fingertips.

8 Continue to breathe in the violet light deeply for two more minutes. And then let that light fade away too.

9 Lie still for a further five minutes. As you do, be aware of the sensations passing through your body.

Once you start this exercise it is better to continue with it on a regular basis. People who have persisted with it for some time report experiencing a feeling of joy and lightness within their bodies. Until our pre-birth traumas are released we cannot feel truly at home in the world, or experience our life as the wonderful adventure it can be.

The Ice Wall –
A Brilliance Technique

This meditation/visualisation process is designed to help you remove inner blocks that restrict you in life and relationships. In terms of colour, it works with brilliance, the pure light.

Emotional experiences and mental attitudes that we took on board in our distant past often create blocks to our enjoyment and freedom today, and it is frequently the case that no amount of realisation or intellectual understanding, or dramatic emotional catharsis, seems to shift them. A deeper level of our psyche must be brought into play.

This process is in two sections: the first part is a visualisation; the second, the dissolving of the Ice Wall.

PART I – VISUALISING

This is the melting ice process. Frozen thoughts create immobility. You can become stuck, it's called a 'safety stand'. The attitude is, 'At least I know where I am.' The only way to free ourselves from these ice blocks is to melt away frozen ideas.

1 First, find a comfortable place where you can be alone and undisturbed.
2 Sit in a relaxed position. Close your eyes and concentrate on your breathing. Notice the coming in of the in-breath and the going out of the out-breath. Become very aware of that small space that occurs between the in-breath and the

out-breath. What happens to you in that U-turn space? Do you go anywhere? Just observe and let go.

When you are breathing gently and without strain, body relaxed, mind at rest, go on to the next step.

3 Visualise yourself warmly dressed in white clothes, sitting in a sleigh at the North Pole. White snow and ice stretch away to the horizon all around you, yet you are not at all cold. The sun is shining and the snowy expanse sparkles beneath the crystal-clear air. The skin on your face tingles from the clean, crisp, cold air. Establish this scene and your place in it strongly.

4 As you sit in your sleigh amidst this scene of purity and light, feel yourself drawing in the sparkling crystal air with every breath. Be aware that the air is filled with light. You are bathed in brilliance, inhaling brilliance.

Allow yourself to stay in this meditation state for several minutes. Let whatever arises in your mind come and go without interference – there are no 'right' or 'wrong' thoughts or feelings. Simply notice what it is coming up in your mind and body.

When you are ready, proceed with the second part of the process.

PART II – DISSOLVING

5 Still sitting, warm and comfortable, in your sleigh amidst the snowy brilliance, visualise a wall of ice slowly rising from the ground in front of you. This wall contains your inner block or blocks.

6 Look at the ice wall closely. Is it cloudy or clear? How high is it? How thick is it? Is it thicker at the bottom of the wall or towards the top? Do not worry yourself with what these mean. It is not necessary for your conscious mind to know

– as something deeper has taken over. Notice that the bright, warm beams of the sun are shining strongly on your wall. Its beams are focused directly on you.

7 As the sun shines, visualise the wall of ice starting to melt. Be very aware that your inner blocks are this wall of ice. Watch as it melts under the power of the sun – drip, drip, drip. This may take some time. It can also be somewhat uncomfortable. Strong feelings may come up. If they do, simply acknowledge them and let them go.

8 When your ice block has melted away, let yourself feel a warmth spreading through your body. That particular block – or blocks – have gone forever!

9 Look at the water from the melted wall. See it as slushy ice. As you look at it, forms start to take shape. These become strong, friendly, white husky dogs shaking their bodies free of slush, and ready to pull your sleigh onwards. Take a deep breath and, as you release it, feel the pull on the reins in your hands as the dogs start to pull the sleigh forward. Let the pure, clean air brush your face and body as you go faster and faster. Feel the exhilarating life coming back into the newly created spaces in your body.

10 Take in a deep breath, and, as you let it out, begin to visualise your sleigh pushing you forward to break through to the consciousness of now. Take several more deep breaths and, as you exhale, begin to come out of this process.

11 Come out very slowly, like a cat having an after-nap stretch.

◆ *As well as being used to clear old blocks, this process can also be used any time you feel your energy has become blocked in your system.*

8

life's colours

Life's colours are the physical, earthly colours of daily existence, exposing your persona from childhood to maturity. They reveal how you motivate and express yourself to the outside world. Similarly you can learn to understand every person who comes across your path!

Colour Your Name

Each name has its own colour. This process enables you to discover what colour your name is, so that you can identify your personality colours. At birth our name is fixed. When our name is called, we recognise the sound; it has its own vibration. As sounds vibrate when our name is called, so our names vibrate to their own colour. A person's name is their colour credential, a colour tag. Our name will have distinctive colour characteristics. Even when our name changes with marriage, the name we were born with will continue to vibrate in conjunction with the new one. The original colour will always have a spiritual bearing throughout our lives. In the Orient, a lot of emphasis is put on the name given to a child. The child's life will be lived trying to become the name. We, too, will vibrate to the colour of our name. All life is vibration.

Use the chart opposite to find your personal name colour and then check the Personality Colours section, which follows on page 259, to understand what your name means and how you can see whether you are working in harmony with your name vibration.

The colour chart is for those of you who like to put things down on paper. It is a way of working with colour that incorporates numbers and the alphabet. Numbers are symbols which represent structure. Life is mathematics in vibrational form. One of our basic needs is structure. Structure gives life form and form gives us safety. By giving ourselves boundaries of form to work with, we can use our energies more efficiently.

In the chart, I have given nine colours. Add numbers over nine together; for example, if you get ten, add one and zero to get one, which is red. I have chosen rose pink for number eight and sun gold for number nine. As number eight would start the beginning of the spectrum colours again, I chose the rich pink as a positive aspect of red and sun gold as a positive aspect of orange. This will provide a wider range of colour meanings from which to work. Turquoise will be represented by the blue and green of the principal hues.

First, write out your name. I have chosen David Brown as an example here. Using the table opposite, find the appropriate number for each letter of your name. Add the numbers together, and keep adding them until you end up with a number between one and nine. As you can see, David's first name adds up to 22, which, by adding two and two, leaves us with four. Now check which colour relates to your number.

David's first name is green. Do the same with your surname. David's surname is gold. Then adding the numbers for his first name (four) and surname (nine), David's overall number is 13 = one + three = four. Check against the table to find your own overall number.

D A V I D   B R O W N
4 1 4 9 4 =22 =4=green   2 9 6 5 5 =27=9=gold

David Brown =4 + 9 = 13 =4 = green

TABLE OF SPECTRUM COLOURS/ PRINCIPAL HUES

Red	1	A	J	S
Orange	2	B	K	T
Yellow	3	C	L	U
Green	4	D	M	V
Blue	5	E	N	W
Indigo	6	F	O	X
Purple	7	G	P	Y
Rose pink	8	H	Q	Z
Sun gold	9	I	R	

NAME COLOUR DEFICIENCY

The next stage is to find out which colours are missing from your name. With David, as you can see, I have written the appropriate number and colour against each letter.

D=4=green   B=2=orange
A=1=red   R=9=sun gold
V=4=green   O=6=indigo
I=9=sun gold   W=5=blue
D=4=green   N=5=blue

Now check how many of each colour you have in your name. David's is shown below:

Red = 1

Orange = 1

Yellow = 0

Green = 3

Blue =2

Indigo = 1

Purple = 0

Rose pink = 0

Sun gold =2

David is lacking in yellow, purple and rose pink. He will need to pay attention to these three colours and incorporate them into his body such as through his diet, décor, visualisation, or any other way that is appropriate for him. The energies these colours produce will be absent from his system, and this will affect his daily life. These missing name colours can give you clues as to why you are not getting what you want from life. They can have an effect on all levels – physical, mental and emotional.

Birth Date Colour

It's great fun and enlightening not only to understand your earthly name energy, but also your birth energy as well. If the two are not compatible it causes conflict in our general, everyday living. For example, if your name is red and your birthdate is red, you may well be living life on a total red over-load! Or, a blue name with an indigo birthdate will cause the person to have problems putting into action any plans, because the blue exerts a restraining influence. For compatibility, check the section on complementaries on page 80.

Your birthdate is fixed, so if your name colour and your birthdate colour are incompatible, you can always change your name! I had a client who said, 'I've never been happy with my name,' and on working out the name and birth date colours I saw the reason why.

To find out your birthdate colour, simply add up the numbers that make up the date (don't forget to add the '19' to the year) and refer back to the colour/number chart on page 257.

You may find your parents' colour vibrations were just perfect for your name colour – or not. It's fun to check out your partner's or friends' names or even a company's name vibration or that of a business colleague to see if they're compatible with your colour. In fact you can check out any word with the chart.

Personality Colours

Having identified the colour of the name or birthdate you are interested in, it's illuminating to check the personality profiles for various areas, listed below.

red

THE RED MALE

Contemplating embarking on a relationship with a red male? Then fasten your seatbelt, because this is going to be a bumpy ride! Think again if your idea of heaven is tea and toast, his slippers ready by the fire, with the idea of watching your favourite soap together on the TV.

'Soap?' he'll say. 'Isn't that the stuff you're going to smooth all over your body and mine while we're in the shower together? And forget the toast. We're going to Paris for dinner tonight – didn't I tell you? Never mind. It won't take you a minute to get ready, and you won't need to pack much for what I've got in mind!'

And it won't, as you are surely not going to miss a minute of being in this red-blooded male's company. Love-making was invented by him. Hadn't you noticed that sensuality oozes from his pores? You'll be wined and dined and made love to for as long as you can keep up the pace – and that will take some doing! You'll forget that he didn't speak to you last night for no reason, but he has to recharge his energies sometime. Or, maybe you put a damper on one of his splendid ideas. To stop a hurricane in full force takes a bit of getting over for a chap like him. But he's here now, and that's all that matters.

Thoughtless and demanding at times he may be, but he is also extremely generous, both materially and in spirit. Just catch up on sleep when he's not around. You'll become the champion of 'cat naps' – and the envy of all your friends. Restless, unpredictable and fiery he may be, but if that match has been struck between you, igniting the flame of love, he'll be your rescuer and saviour forever. What more could a girl want?

THE RED FEMALE

Now here is a red dynamo if ever there was one: she can match a man anytime, anywhere – or so she thinks. If you are thinking of wooing that woman dashing about over there in the red dress, well, go ahead, but put on your crash helmet first, and be prepared to walk over a bed of red-hot coals while journeying along the path of love with this firecracker. You could get burnt, but it will be such fun and so exciting to try, and on the other hand you could end up with only a blister or two. Just *thinking* about it is exhilarating.

Top-of-the-mountain moments can come your way with this tomato. She'll be straightforward and honest with you. Manipulation is not her style; she knows how to play the game of relationships. Why waste time beating about the bush when her motto is, 'If you want it, go and get it!' Subtlety is not her speciality, so forget little intimacies. If she wants you, you'll know about it, and she'll shout it from the rooftops.

One tiny flaw, perhaps, is that she'll expect no lies from you either. It's best to not let this lady's temper explode. Deceit is a surefire way to erupt this latent volcano. When a love affair is over, she will not be malicious; she has the secret of knowing that she has the capacity to fall in love over and over again. Red-hot passion was invented by Ms Red. You'll be the envy of every male around if you are the right one for her, and she's decided to let her embers glow permanently with you. She'll swap that red dress for a pair of red shoes instead and support and protect you and her babies forever. Hell and high water will not deter her from keeping her treasured loved ones safe and secure.

THE RED PARENT

Mrs Red mother says to her offspring: 'That didn't hurt now, did it?' as she dismissively gives her darling a little rub on the huge, egg-sized lump that is appearing on his forehead, the consequence of having fallen from the top bunk bed.

'Mum, it hurts,' he protests.

'Don't be silly,' she says, wiping his tears away. 'Get back up there again and see if you can walk along the edge again. Only this time don't fall off.'

And he doesn't: 'Wow this is great. I can do anything.' With parents relating to red energy, who could fail to achieve!

Very ambitious for their children, no barriers will exist that they will not be able to remove if it means advancement for their offspring. Woebetide any bullying that their progeny has endured. The culprit won't do it again once Mum or Dad Red has dealt with it. A few choice words blown into the offender's ear scares the living daylights out of them.

Not one for sentiments, their motto for their child is: 'Keep your emotions hidden, kid. That's the best way to be if you want to get on in this world.' They forget that they have frequent outbursts of temper themselves when they are thwarted, particularly when their emotions have been hurt – but that's them though, isn't it! Oblivious to the receiver of their wrath lying wounded on the floor, it wasn't intentional and no one got anywhere without discipline did they!? A hug and it will soon be better – and it is.

Surviving the adventurous, fast, chaotic upbringing that a red parent provides will equip you with the tools to surmount anything that future life will throw your way.

THE RED CHILD

If the stork delivers to your house a baby born with the influence of the red colour, then forget the word 'sleep' for the next two years. In fact, it would have been wise to have enjoyed your months of pregnancy, as they were your last! They were not your last months on this Earth of course, but they will be your quietest before Miss or Master Red leaves home at 18 for college. When this little bundle of dynamite hits the scene your life will be a continuous whirlpool. If you want a quiet, placid baby, then don't place his arrival in April, the month of Aries, or give him a red-resonating name.

Mind you, it is not all a disaster. This little mite will give you such excitement, as he drags you up to the top of the highest cliff, and, wherever you go, you will always be the centre of attention, because *he* (or *she*) is.

Don't despair. Go along with this helter-skelter ride. This

darling red rose of a tomboy that is your daughter, or your son the flame-thrower, will give you back your youth all over again. At time when the seat of parenthood gets too hot with your charging red dynamo, just remind yourself as they leave for day nursery: only 15 more years to go! Then suddenly they'll drop their lunch box and school bag full of noisy toys and fling their arms around you and shout: 'I love you Mum', and you won't be able to wait for that little darling firecracker to return home. Without that red ray of energy in your life it's too quiet around the house! In their teens, he or she will be the leader of the gang. They won't be able to hold on to their pocket money because they are a soft touch for the underdog. Keep them interested; never allow them to get bored, and they will pioneer their way into your and everyone else's heart.

THE RED BOSS

Finding yourself hired to work for a boss who functions on the energy of red will definitely ensure a lively work environment. Full of energy, zest and drive, there won't be a dull moment in the office. Down to earth and forthright, he'll always cut to the quick. No hanging about in this workplace. His energy will be inexhaustible; he'll be relentless in pursuit of his goals – and he'll expect the same of you. The red female entrepreneur will be just as driven, and can crack the whip harder and longer. She is a master at using her feminine wiles to achieve her goals. Nine-to-five does not exist in their calendar: you'll be expected to work when needs must.

The red boss takes you at face value; as long as you do the job, that's all that matters. Be smart: don't practise your coochy-coo games with them. Be honest. Dare to present your whacky ideas. If they could work, they're the ones who can push them through. Be loyal, and you'll be rewarded well. As long as you don't try to outshine them, you'll definitely be acknowledged for your contributions. Get plenty of sleep, take extra vitamins, even a course at the gym, to improve your stamina; you've got to find a way to keep up with this whirlpool of a boss. Just remember, it will always be exciting, even if they do bully a little, and can be a pain in the behind at times. In the workspace, the red boss's motto is: 'Seize the day, always' – and you will.

THE RED EMPLOYEE

The key problem when hiring someone who works on the red energy ray is restlessness. A challenge is what is required. Just point him or her in the direction where you have a hassle, and they'll sort it out for you. You see, the red employee must keep moving, always striving for clarity and smooth running. Just don't expect them to sit there doing nothing.

Not wishing to stick to regular hours need not be a problem, as they'll always make up time and give you extra on top. Call them in a crisis – they love it! He or she is equally good at keeping people happy on all sides. Be sincere in your praise of them, because they can smell a dum-dum anytime.

Red employee's are only marking time until they can either step into their boss's job, or set up their own business, as self-employment really suits them best. Not wishing to stab you in the back, nonetheless they will step happily into anyone's shoes whom they feel does not match up to the job. If you are the boss, a wise move would be to make them a partner immediately! The business will flourish in leaps and bounds, and anyway, it's always a good move to make the enemy your friend. Best to keep an eye on red employees if you can. Where did they say they were going? What for? Does anyone know what they are doing? Don't worry. They'll probably be back carrying the goodies along with the contract you were hoping to get signed, sealed and delivered.

orange

THE ORANGE MALE

This man is a free spirit. He is, for want of another word, promiscuous. Beware of becoming too serious and heavy with this orange-motivated lover. If it's wedding bells you're after, then go seek a more stable mate in the romance department. He will have been frank with you from the beginning and won't have led you up the garden path. If you pause to think about the obvious clues he always gave you during this liaison, it was never, ever going to be anything other than just a bit of fun. Let's face it. You were originally attracted to his flamboyance. He was the one standing there in the centre of the room surrounded by twittering females. Mr Orange is the perfect lover, particularly if you are a married woman looking for just a bit of spare time activity.

Socialising and friendliness are the name of the game for Mr Genial Orange, so if you are the jealous type, he is not for you. You'll have to be prepared to go along with his spirit of freedom or you'll stay at home alone. The key is to let him know that you must have your freedom too, as he has the habit of thinking that you and your time are reserved exclusively for him. But watch out if he finds that you are not waiting for him in the exact spot where he left you at the party, with a sweet expression on your face – after he suddenly becomes disenchanted flirting with the available company.

Although he values friendship and warmheartedness in a girl he also admires a woman who presents a challenge to him. He has high standards when settling for a female for life. The clinging vine is not his forte. The independent smart lady is just up his street. 'Wow! Maybe she'll go on safari with me!' He loves animals you see, and children, as you find out later on. All that open space and fresh air is just marvellous.

Don't think the wilderness will knock him out and get him scurrying early to bed, because it won't! Just let him sit down with a drink for a few minutes and he'll be ready with all his energy back again to foray out into the midnight jungle air. He is a pack animal, and he'll hunt anytime, particularly if there are pretty girls there. So, after you've put your tracking gear away, get your party dress ready. Perhaps you should have a stiff drink too, but one thing's for sure, you're definitely going to be in the land of the living with this dynamic, exciting, unpredictable man.

THE ORANGE FEMALE

When it comes to relationships for the female embued with the orange ray, it's difficult to tell who is the hunter and who is being hunted! You see, Ms Orange feels she can do anything her male counterpart can do, if not better, and she cannot abide weakness in a man. Quick to take action, she doesn't believe in putting off for tomorrow what can be done today – and that includes you! There really is little to choose between the orange male or female except that she is more patient at breaking down barriers, particularly in business.

She is a master at practical knowledge because she uses her intuition psychically, her gut instincts. She can bring clear, logical treatment to every situation. She is very forthright in her dealings with men, and honest to a fault with a lover. Because she values her independence so much, she will not compromise herself. So a strong man is necessary as she may need a little restraining at times, particularly when she gets carried away with new projects such as the idea of adding a new extension to the house when there is only enough room for a small shed! You see, she believes it is possible, and that if you only put your mind to it and persevere enough, it can materialise.

She loves changes: the furniture will be constantly moved around the house. Although she is sporty and loves to exercise, she will always need a little restraining where food is concerned, particularly if she is bored. Food and drink will be used as comforts, which ultimately creates a weight problem.

Never tell her to do anything. Ask her. She won't take to being bullied or pushed around. It may be difficult when embarking on a relationship with Ms Orange to tell whether she wants you for a friend or lover. 'Aren't they both the same?' she'll retort. She'll never let you see her cry, but she does in private while she tries to fathom out what she said that upset you so. She didn't intend to; it's just that she is blunt, and can't tell lies. Restless by nature, she prefers the lads as mates rather than sisterhood. Girlie chat is not her idea of heaven. House budgeting is not her strongest point either: better that you pay the bills.

She loves the unexpected. Routine will bring about claustrophobia. She must have a challenge. There is never a dull moment if you are on a par with her. A sparring partner is what is required. Just keep surprising her and you'll have the best friend ever, as well as a passionate lover. She has no difficulties expressing herself in that area!

THE ORANGE PARENT

Of all the colours of the rainbow the orange parent loves parenthood the most. It is said the greatest gift you can give your child is time, and the orange Mum and Dad certainly will; but they will also give their children the gift of enthusiasm. The children – there will always be more than one! – will be encouraged to approach each and every aspect in their lives with spirit. When little Tommy loses the ball game yet again, the child will be reminded that a bad patch is just a learning curve, and can be used as a time for advancement.

Every cloud has its silver lining – and don't come home if you lose next time!

Many hobbies and team games will be encouraged as orange parents believe that variety is the spice of life. But they must take care to train their child to complete a task before moving on to the next. Once orange ray individuals have decided to start a family, they will always keep the marriage together for the sake of the children. They find divorce abhorrent. Mother Orange, although she is a good cook, won't want to be stuck in the kitchen when she can be out there playing with her cubs. She'll become their big sister and they will adore her forever. Orange parents do not produce prissy kids, although perhaps sons are more suited to the boisterous and sometimes clumsy behaviour of orange Dad. If he has a daughter he will discover her later on when she's old enough to be proudly shown off on his arm, displayed to the world. He will then treat her as a fragile china doll, forgetting that she has been swinging on ropes and roughing it with her brothers for the last 16 years.

Both orange parents enjoy their children as they get older and will treat them as pals. Orange parents are lax with discipline until they lose their tempers for five minutes. Their offspring will sprint for cover and hide until the outburst is over, but it quickly passes and all is forgotten.

Sometimes it's hard for children to meet the demands of orange parents; it's just that Mum and Dad are so keen to give them every opportunity. Optimism is the child's experience with these parents. They remain full of youth and joy, perpetually acting like a little bird that has just broken out of its egg. It's sometimes hard to fathom out who is the parent and who is the child!

THE ORANGE CHILD

No one rests while a little orange sunbeam is around. They require your undivided attention because of all that constant questioning.

Your orange son will never want to be left alone either. He needs an audience – it's essential that he is in the thick of it; not necessarily the centre of attention all the time, but all that activity makes him feel secure. Your orange baby girl is just as demonstrative, and quite capable of displaying her determin-ation of purpose if her sweet cooing doesn't get a direct response. Just remember he or she will always be sunny as can be if surrounded by noise, hustle and bustle, provided they are never banished to the nursery at bedtime when young. Just put the crib in the middle of the room when you're having a party, and I promise you they'll sleep like a baby!

Orange kids are prone to accidents, as adventure is a key feature, so keep a constant supply of Elastoplasts handy. And it's best not to warn the new child-minder that you keep your little darling chained up to stop him killing himself while he scales the outside wall of the house, so that he can sit on the roof and figure out how the birds fly. After all, Batman can do it, so why not him?

Orange children are usually able to combat most childhood ailments with ease even if they appear quite delicate. They are extremely malleable unless someone hurts their feelings; then run for cover if this mini-volcano blasts off. School and college pose no problems, as they love to learn and can absorb facts quickly, particularly mathematics. And they are usually excellent at sports.

In their teens they spend money freely and won't give a jot what people think. Why provoke him by challenging his over-spending? He's a free spirit. Even so, his loyalty to you as his parents will be unequalled. When others notice you've started

to put on a few pounds and parts of you have started to journey south, you'll always be gorgeous in your orange
offspring's eyes, and that will be for keeps.

THE ORANGE BOSS

If you find yourself working for Ms or Mr Orange, learn quickly
that detail is not their forte – it is yours. That's what they
hired you for. They will be working on their latest grand vision
and will be engaged in sweeping lines of expansion. No point
in thinking too much before you leap with this boss. If his
enthusiasm has been sparked off for a new project – particularly if it is unusual, or better still way-out – then it's all
stations go! But orange bosses can be erratic, and never stick
to schedules, and they are constantly alert for that next
contract that could be the big one. As far as the orange boss
is concerned, materialistic opportunity knocks, and it will do
so right at his front door!

The orange boss has his own way of doing things; unfortunately, he doesn't always get around to enlightening you.
You'll just have to run along with it as best you can, or wait
until he returns (he loves to travel) to put you in the picture.
Working for him, you have to be on tip toes constantly, as he's
quick to criticise, which deflates you. But he'll then throw you
that dazzling smile of his unexpectedly and say 'well done' for
all that overtime you've put in for the last three weeks, just
when you thought he hadn't noticed. It's irritating when he
expects to be obeyed instantly, but his bark is really worse
than his bite.

Orange bosses are quick and smart; never forget facts and
figures. They have an uncanny instinct for where it's happening, and real business acumen. They have the knack of breaking through barriers. Orange bosses are great believers in
further education, particularly if you, the employee, is doing

it! Nothing about you or your private life will be unknown –
your secrets will be wheedled from you. He or she will help
you where possible if you have domestic problems.

He draws towards himself those lucrative deals because he
can see the whole picture, and is an astute bargain hunter in
business. A great entrepreneur because of his breadth of
vision, fortunately, he is born lucky where money is concerned.
If he lost a pound from his pocket this morning, he'll find a
£50 note walking home that evening.

The orange boss has great pride in achievement, and
wants to be recognised for it – perhaps a small Oscar, or, why
not a bigger one? Whatever, you can rest assured that at any
receptions that may occur, you'll be right there sitting along-
side your exuberant boss, sharing the champagne with the
best of them.

THE ORANGE EMPLOYEE

You are lucky indeed if you have managed to hire a Mr or Ms
Orange. Anything that needs enthusiasm and push will suit
the orange worker well. They are brilliant salesmen, but be
sure the merchandise is what it says – they are not about
promoting rubbish. It's that integrity rearing up again; robbers
they are not! Give them the project, send them out with a
suitcase full of samples, and before you can turn around
they're back with a fist full of money.

The orange grafters don't need things to be explained twice;
they're there before you are. They work best being part of a
team; they work hard, and play hard. Just keep him or her
busy. Take him into your confidence and appreciate his input –
which means pay him well, as he spends as soon as he gets.
He'll be the employee you won't want to do without. Against all
odds, he turns up trumps. If you ever have to gamble all you
have on a roll of the dice, let the orange guy or girl throw it!

Stretch him, but don't abuse. Listen to that hunch of his, as he is born under a lucky star. He can also be exasperating at times, as it is difficult for him to take orders. But just when you've had enough, he'll come up with a brilliant tactic that becomes the company's saving grace yet again. If he does decide he's been affronted, he'll leave without a backward glance. His Achilles' heel is cash – he always needs it, now! If you're tight, he'll say 'goodnight', and that would be a pity, as you'll never be able to replace him again. It will be your loss.

yellow

THE YELLOW MALE

Mr Yellow's personality makes for a very 21st century-oriented male. Mr Smart Guy resides under the colour yellow. To him the chase can be worth more than the catch, and it usually is. He just loves to spar intellectually with you. It's impossible to win an argument with him because of his agility of mind. His idea of romance is to take you to a trendy restaurant full of celebrities; or better still, racing drivers, as he loves fast cars. The menu will be unusual, which won't be poured over for long, as food is not a priority. You'll be whisked off to a marvellously interesting soirée, and after drinks at about 2a.m., it will suddenly occur to him to maybe engage in a little extra-curricular activity – and that is you! He is broadminded when it comes to your behaviour; it will be so even in the bedroom. If you want to try it, he'll go along. Forget foreplay – you've had that already as far as he is concerned. He's taken you out for the last six hours and that should be enough! You don't want to go to bed on your first date? That's OK. He won't be offended. Tomorrow's another day, and he does have to be at the stock exchange – or the office, or the shop floor for that matter – in a few hours' time. Yellows are the classic workaholics.

Mr Yellow can't stand clinging vines so if you're looking for security in your romance, forget it. The action is always where he happens to be at the moment. He will uncover your inner-most secrets in two seconds flat, and just when you thought you were getting really cosy and intimate, he has to go on a business trip. Then, Hey Presto!, there was this fascinating little lady he just happened to chat to, and bang, you are yesterday's news. Of course, he just might return to you, particularly if you kept a few secrets back, which has kept him guessing; he can't resist intrigue, or, if you have a pret-tier face! He just melts at the sight of facial beauty.

Constantly restless, travel becomes the yellow male's recreational pursuit, along with photography. He seems to have a dual personality: the love of life and the love of you. You never know if he will turn up grumpy or a little ray of sunlight. Anyway, what does it matter as long as he does turn up! One thing is sure: you'll never want to miss being on board with this fast-moving missile. He can fly from rags to riches. Now that's a trip to be pencilled in any girl's calendar.

THE YELLOW FEMALE

This woman most surely resonates with the line 'Life's is too short to stuff a mushroom'. There will be no hours spent in the kitchen. She's never heard of a thermometer to test the sauce. That's something you put in your mouth when you're ill, isn't it? She's rarely sick, so she won't experience that either. She will, however, introduce you to the most unusual, fascinating place that's 'just divine, darling', with the most interesting people. What's the food like? She won't know – it's far too interesting a place to eat!

Yellow is the colour of the slimmer: she abhors fat because it slows her down. You'd better get yourself in trim if you want to keep up with her. She's a modern miss who simply follows the latest fashion, although she is inclined to clutter up her appearance with too many separates that do not co-ordinate. You can wear something bizarre too – she won't mind! She loves colour more than most, even experimenting with her hair and make-up shades and tints. She may make a few mistakes but it will be dramatic, if perhaps a little startling: she loves to shock.

Ms Yellow is such fun to be with, a laugh a minute; if you want heavy, drama-laden romance, forget it, she's not for you. Intimacy can be difficult, as she's far too busy. Possessing a quicksilver temperament, she can take a bit of catching. She will have many acquaintances, even get engaged many times. It will take a very special knight to catch her for good. She may appear to have a butterfly mind, but don't be fooled. She is not an air-head; she can literally think of two things at once.

Gambling attracts yellows as well as counselling, as they have a knack of pinpointing the issues. A great journalist, she can squeeze information from a stone. She is an explorer of all avenues of life, and that will include you. A lady of many facets, she is extremely vivacious, but gets confused when she finds herself in love with two people at the same time. When she finally commits, you can be very sure you are a very special man. She will be prepared to go anywhere and do anything for her chosen male's desire. You'll go through a gauntlet of emotions every single day, but keep your yellow lady-love always looking forwards, and the both of you will never look back.

THE YELLOW PARENT

Yellow parents have no problem with the generation gap as they remain kids themselves forever. Although the yellow-aspected mother will be fascinated by her new baby, having an aversion to monotony, she will have a tendency to become bored quickly with the daily routine. This is the one female most suited to combining parenthood with a career. She can juggle both extremely well. This way she can enjoy her little bundle of joy's antics and the inquisitive period to come later on. The challenge of motherhood will be channelled into fun rather than frustration.

Both yellow parents will keep the house full of toys, books and videos to stretch their child's imagination. Yellow parents are extremely interested in education, and hence are inclined to cram too much into junior's head too soon. They will need to keep in mind that a two-year-old will only have a limited attention span, and that college is still some time away yet! They also know the value of life's experiences, and become determined that their child will have plenty of that.

Convinced that junior is a genius, it never occurs to Dad that the child's pleas to become a farmer and not a lawyer have any relevance. He will also keep him physically active, believing that exercise is good for the soul as well as the waistline! Kids of yellow parents usually don't get fat, as food is not high up on the agenda – no family get-togethers here over meals. It's more like grab a sandwich on the run.

It can sometimes be difficult for children to get a grip on what the house rules are, as the boundaries seem to change every day. Yellows are the most inclined to adopt children; the more the merrier, as they just love young people. It's great to be the offspring of a yellow parent, particularly as they are so lax with the rules, and will avoid chastisement of any kind; although this can also result in the spoiled brat brigade of kids. Another plus to being brought up by yellow power is when teenagers want to flee the nest, as there is an understanding that you are only young once. In this household love and laughter will prevail, and imagination will be stretched to the limit. 'That's a smart kid,' the world will say to Mr and Mrs Yellow. 'Of course,' will be the reply. How could they be anything else? Lucky children!

THE YELLOW CHILD

Your little baby ray of sunshine will be a delightful addition to the family, full of fun, joy and laughter. Later on they will need to be taught discernment, as they will go off with anyone if their imagination is triggered. They are so creative that they can easily confuse fantasy with reality, and can tell 'porky pies' (lies) with no intention of fibbing at all.

As children, sleep seems to elude them. They are naturally razor-sharp, and extremely active. It's best to wear them out with energetic play so that a healthy tiredness will follow, rather than trying to slow them down, which will lead to frustration and moodiness.

Friendly show-offs, you never know what their response will be to new encounters. They don't know themselves. They embrace you each day with renewed gusto, a tornado of enthusiasm. They are Mummy's little dare-devils, who love to take risks.

They are quick students, and can actually challenge many a school or college teacher. Lovers of words, they seem to have been born running, talking and streetwise. There may be a need for guidance to complete tasks, as there is an inclination to jump from one project to another. Keep them focused, as they only have the concentration span of a gnat! In time they will master many areas, and are naturally drawn to the media, eventually making excellent newscasters because of their wide span of general knowledge – it's all those evenings spent doing homework and listening to the radio at the same time. This budding yellow energy produces the future racing driver. He's already had enough practice crashing into your furniture in his toy car. The quieter ray of yellow sunshine could become a car mechanic. Miss Yellow will have been practising her verbal skills to attain her future goals.

They'll both keep you on your toes and have you in fits of laughter with their mimicry. I think you have got it by now – the idea of restriction is alien to them. Freewheelers, that's what they are, so let them go! go! go! It may be a bumpy ride for the parents, but it will be a journey to remember in your heart forever – and you will, with love and joy.

THE YELLOW BOSS

Expansion is the name of the game for Boss Yellow. He has no hesitation to replace you if you don't come up to scratch, he does not suffer fools gladly. Never short of a word or two, yellows will strive until the goal is accomplished. Leaving no stone unturned, exploring all avenues, they will unravel and reveal until the issue that will get the desired results has been pinpointed. Great inventors, they are analytical, born critics, because they are clever at getting to the core of the matter. They are drawn to the media as they love gossip. Organised crime can attract them too – anything where they need their wits about them. If harsh justice is needed, they are prepared to run a company as a liquidator – they'll cut through the red tape. You cannot be a malingerer working for a yellow boss. He has talent and can become a workaholic, which can either lead to the stars or to a breakdown by sheer exhaustion. He or she executes plans instantly, with charm and persuasion if needs be. They are big thinkers where it comes to money. The old way of doing things is not for them: tradition belongs to the past. Reason is the name of the game, compassion is not: 'I'm running a company, not a kindergarten'. Appearing at times callous, their motto is: 'There is no love lost where business is concerned. You are either with me or you are not.'

They possess an agility of mind, so do not attempt to outsmart this boss because you won't. If you feel you can, then you should be self-employed. This mental dictator may seem impossible to work for. But before you type your resignation a head will appear from his office door with that impish smile and suggest you take the day off! They are social geniuses – they have such style and wit. Many a deal is clinched over a drink. There won't be any part of the organisation that he doesn't know about, and that includes you.

He may be incorrigible and exasperating, even callous, but stick with him. Tears won't budge him, so make him laugh. That will! The yellow boss has the Midas touch, the genie with the magic lamp into the commercial world. Just one little rub from his golden fingers and, Hey Presto, all his employees' dreams come true. It will be yours in your pay packet when the next Christmas bonus comes around.

THE YELLOW EMPLOYEE

The disposition of your yellow employee can be summed up as sunny and willing but fickle and unreliable. Any job that requires communication is best suited. They just love PR, networking, and wheeling and dealing on the phone. Incognito is not for them; they demand to be involved and noticed. Clear, precise thinking is a gift of theirs, always looking for fresh angles. They are a store of information because everything must add up.

Both the sexes are snappy dressers, always creating the latest image. Such chatterboxes, they have everyone around them in stitches of laughter. It can be a joke a minute with seemingly not a lot of work being done, but don't be fooled by that. They've already done it! They make marvellous up-front people, such as a liaison officer, where great flair is required. Great in the hospitality business, they believe you should always leave a sweet taste in the mouth of the client. They may not get the required result today, but having left such a good feeling behind them, when they've figured out how to get what they want, there will be no obstacles when they make the next contact. Their minds are always having a workout where clear, precise thinking is essential.

They won't work for a boss who is disorganised. As they are great problem solvers, it is hard for anyone to pull the wool over their eyes. If they lose respect for you, or the policies of the company leave them cold, they will not hesitate to depart. You're only a stepping stone anyway to them becoming their own boss, the job that they *really* want. Make no mistake: Mr or Ms Yellow will always be looking to the main chance, which is themselves. Although they appear to be free spenders, they will always remember that a fool and his money are soon parted, and fools they are not.

They respond well to pressure; how good for the boss when everyone else seems to be making a break for the toilet! They have been paying attention after all, and stashing away in their minds every aspect that they knew would become useful in a future crisis! Yellow believes the future is now; they can't wait for tomorrow. A walking talking filing cabinet – every office should have one!

green

THE GREEN MALE

Mr Green is one big, gorgeous, hunk of masculinity, with a romantic soul. As the green colour is ruled by Venus, the goddess of love, you can expect to have hit it lucky in this relationship. You couldn't ask for a more romantic and charming liaison. You can expect to be wined and dined at the most expensive restaurants and showered with delightful gifts and luxuries under cloud green.

Once you hit the sack after a respectable period of time has passed – as Mr Green does not like to be rushed – you won't be disappointed either, as green's vibrations represents replenishment of the earth – what could be more important than that? So why not give it your full attention and enjoy sensual pleasures to the full. Attracted strongly to the opposite sex, nonetheless aggressive pursuit is not his bag of tricks; but subtlety is, because he fully enjoys the ritual of coupling. You may need to make the first move. It's not that your green lover is particularly shy, its just that he doesn't want to waste time going after someone who is not interested. Honest from the start, they do not believe in tricky, sharp manoeuvring in the mating game. What you see is what you get, even if it does take them a while to get going. Not prone to wearing their hearts on their sleeves, you could think perhaps they are a little dull! Don't make that mistake: he's weighing you up slowly. This man is about marriage. A future partner for life is what he is after, and he *means* life! He will shower you with all his worldly goods, even if it does make him a workaholic to acquire them. But once the deal is done, it is straight home for him.

The way to his heart is to wear soft, glamorous clothes and exotic perfume. He is a very touchy-feely person. You'll be in the kitchen a lot as he loves his food, but as he's also chosen you for your down-to-earthness, he'll expect you to help him watch his weight, which can be a real problem. Harmony in the home is paramount: discord and divorce will send him scurrying to the hills. His aim is to acquire a beautiful house where you can entertain if you feel like it. It will be his castle and you will be his queen. Just make sure that green's possessiveness does not make it a prison. Having captured his mate, he regards her as 'his', which could smother the relationship. You're on to a winner if it's love, marriage and babies you're after. He'll provide you with security come what may. Nowhere else will you engage such consideration and affection. To be cherished so until eternity is truly a many splendoured thing, in the green, green grass of home.

THE GREEN FEMALE

Ms Green flirts her way through life from the moment she opens her lovely eyes at birth, and continues to do so to the grave. She won't be able to abide greyness and decay. In her Will, she will leave specific instructions that she is to look her best. 'Just dress me in pink dear, and don't forget the lip gloss! After all, you never know who you might meet where I'm going! I wonder if the Angel Gabriel likes blondes or brunettes?' You see? She can't help it.

Although she is preoccupied with her femininity, initially on meeting the opposite sex she gives the impression of being an ice maiden because of her calmness and restraint. However, once smitten she truly draws upon those hidden fires of passion. Whatever she does in life will have a measure of sensuality involved. A lover of perfume, flowers and nature, she has the ability to be a farmhand by day, and turn into a temptress in the bedroom at night. She adores luxury but is not a gold-digger; if you can't supply it, she can.

Not having been drawn to study for the sake of it in her early years, nonetheless she knows how to make money if she has to. This is a down-to-earth female who has a natural-born gift to bring romance to the seemingly mundane. Much as she strives to bring balance and beauty to all she encounters in life, if fate pushes her into dire straits or adversity, you can rely on her. Ms Green comes to the fore when coping; she is the practical idealist. Her agreeability always bridges the gap. She is most amenable. Like a reed bending in the wind, she is adaptable.

You are lucky indeed if this sexy, salt-of-the-earth lady chooses you. She'll forgive you your little foibles so many times, as long as you make sure you don't wink too much at the opposite sex at social gatherings. She doesn't like to be teased or fooled around with, either. Once the match of her desire has been struck within her heart, she'll smoulder and burn passionately forever, if that's what you want too! As Shakespeare said: 'They do not love who do not show they love.' If you've managed to snare a green goddess, once smitten she will demonstrate her love for you in that beautiful home she creates, till the end of time.

THE GREEN PARENT

Green is nature's wheel of opportunity, and these parents will make sure that their children will not miss out. Because they can see both sides of any issue they have a tendency to weigh things up constantly. Their children may feel that they moralise, but there is a fear of not being good enough as parents, which makes them extremely conscientious. Perfectionist where their children are concerned, they do not always practise what they preach. A more dutiful mother you will not find, nursing her sick child back to health whatever it takes. She likes routine and will encourage her kids to bring their friends home after school, where a sumptuous snack will await on the dot. Both parents will encourage their offspring to develop early any talents they may possess – dance classes, music, gardening, anything physical. Father Green can be quite strict when it comes to discipline, and will teach his kids right from wrong from the beginning. He is rigid with the idea that there is one rule for the boys and another, lenient, one for the girls. Nonetheless the son will get a fair deal, and any daughter will be totally cherished. His kids might think he is a square and boring, but the truth is he is better with them once they have grown up and out of their teens, and have stopped challenging his beliefs. However, hell hath no fury as green parents when provoked into defending their young.

To be blessed with parents under the green hue can be delightful. Both will be patient and will, if necessary, go to work to provide material luxuries for their loved ones. These parents become a security blanket for these children, which is never removed. Opportunity really has knocked at your door if fate has landed you where you get a green upbringing. The kids soon learn that the grass will never be greener anywhere else in the world. Home life will truly have been the best.

THE GREEN CHILD

Children of the green colour can best be summed up as the settled, contented babies – calm and tranquil, smiling sweetly and quietly in their crib, and obligingly compliant with the daily routine as long as their basic needs are met. Sounds too good to be true? Well, not really. If you are as in tune with the rhythm of life as they are, then they're no bother. You couldn't wish for happier, easier babies, but cross them unwisely and you'll hear a bellow from them that could bring the house down! They appear a little timid, but respond wonderfully to affection and encouragement. From an early age they realise that peace is best.

At school they will co-operate and be attentive, if appearing a little slow. Don't be fooled. It's just that they have the ability to weigh things up immediately but don't feel the need to make a fuss about their knowledge. When the chips are down, somehow Master or Miss Green will always have a little in reserve, even secret cash hidden in their piggy bank! Watch out too, when you play Monopoly with them!

These kids love being children; they don't want to be mini-grownups. That will come all in good time. Take them out into the country, preferably with a puppy of their own, and they couldn't be happier. Both kids will be tomboys. He will forever be exploring new pastures; his little green sister will be tagging right along – she prefers to play with the fellas. She may even introduce a game or two of 'kiss-chase' just to exercise her femininity, keeping in reserve the full force of her charms for later.

These children are a delight to raise, seldom moody unless unhappy, when they lose their appetite and love of food. They are liberal with their hugs and kisses unless pushed, when they will become stiff and unmovable. Just suggest they do an exciting project and do it with kindness, and love and light will reign again.

These children are extremely sensitive to their surroundings. Colours that harmonise with rhythmic music affects their psyche tremendously. These tender green children have hidden talents. When the time is right they'll burst forth like a little seed from its husk and become that tall, strong, sturdy tree that the universe can lean on. The apples never fall far from the orchard, and your little green babes will always be with you to comfort you forever.

THE GREEN BOSS

At the end of the day, what Mr and Ms Green boss expect from you is productivity. What's the point of pursuing something if there's nothing to show for it? If it doesn't work, he or she will just tell you to recycle and produce – that's the key. The male boss will consider all angles and tie up loose ends, because carelessness leads to failure – which leads to poverty! They are generous bosses indeed when the company does well. They rarely go bankrupt, as something is always held back for a rainy day. As green is made up of yellow and blue, there is sometimes a conflict of whether to go for it, yellow's influence, or cool it, the blue side. The challenge is to keep a balance when decision making.

The green boss, male or female, loves luxury and wealth, which means you'll probably work in glamorous surroundings. But they are not spendthrifts, and they won't expect you to waste the company's time or money. Please them and you may get an invitation to a drinks party in their lovely home with its lavish furnishings and impressive paintings. Greens adore beauty and money in its material form. This boss fares well as a farmer, in real estate, industry, or as an entrepreneur. Green is the colour of finance. Their greatest asset is common sense, and their word is their bond. Although always acting from caution, when Boss Green finally says 'I'm ready to roll now,' it really means 'Get out of my way!'.

You may think they are pushovers – the mistake will be yours. They'll give you enough rope to see if you hang yourself, or can manage to climb back aboard again. If not, you're fired. Working for them brings improvement for all concerned. It can be a very pleasant, well-organised experience. There won't be too much gushing or too many compliments flying around, but if you stay loyal to them you will have job security for as long as it pleases you. You receive big bonuses, own your own car and property, and can look forward to a substantial pension for life – and you won't end up with shattered nerves or angina either! This boss will have brought prosperity into your life in more ways than one.

THE GREEN EMPLOYEE

If diplomacy is required from an employee, here is your man – or woman. They are definitely not your fly-by-night hustlers: smart and reserved, and honest with it. When he/she believes in you, the boss, and in the work at hand, they will give it their undivided attention until it is completed. They do not need to be guided every step of the way. Just tell them what you're aiming for and leave it with them – they will fill in the cracks. They are able to take your orders with good grace, because they know that one day they will be giving them. But much as you can burden these workers with a lot of responsibility, do not abuse. They will constantly come up trumps for you, but if they feel offended by your attitude, and that their contribution is not respected, they will simply quit. You will truly have deserved it. They can be pushed, but not flattened.

Both sexes are absolutely ace when it comes to sorting out a crisis, revelling in bringing calm and serenity to a seemingly lost cause. Patience is their virtue, and they will listen to hours of clients' boring chat, waiting to get that signature, and they do. Great employees to have in the office, they always dress well. Much as they are drawn to creative, glamorous work in the luxury trades, their feet are firmly on the ground. They aim high, because they want the good things in life. They are not arrogant, cannot abide conceit in others, and are adept in taking anyone down a peg or two – including you, the boss, before they leave! They can't bear to be humiliated either, so it's not wise to provoke them unless you like witnessing the rare experience of a silent breeze turning into a destructive tornado.

The way to secure the continuous output of green's advantageous energy for your company is to ensure they get a regular pay packet and receive annual raises without them having to beg for it. They know their place. You are the boss and they will fulfil their part being the employee. Treat them well; a little kindness goes a long way. As the saying goes, you catch more flies with honey than you ever will with vinegar.

blue

THE BLUE MALE

This man is a believer in love at first sight. He's in love with love – flighty, emotional, romantic and charming. As he is inclined to view romance through rose-coloured spectacles, he can be blind to your faults and, indeed, his own. If you're looking for a whirlwind affair, then this is it! Mr Blue will sweep you up into a haze of delight, proclaiming love forever, and showering you with compliments. What more could you want? Not a lot, if you're going to remain on the treadmill as lovers. If marriage is embarked upon, much as every effort will be made to supply financially for the family, the realities of the outside world can represent quite a challenge. If necessary, be prepared on the monetary front to make arrangements to take things into your own hands – i.e. going out to work – when the bills have to be paid. The intention will be there, but if times become hard he will hide his head in the sand and hope that tomorrow will somehow resolve itself. He is highly creative, but he can be easily swayed by emotion and intuition. Depending on how he feels on the day, he can be a real sucker for a hard-luck story. On another day, wild horses couldn't make him part with a penny!

He is ruled by a sense of destiny and purpose, and doesn't realise that there are bodily needs that have to be met, requiring the acquisition of money. It could be argued that he is self-deceptive, but it's because of this willingness to be kind to all and sundry that he shelves the unpleasant. This man needs space – he can't stand being confined. He may disappear for a while, but don't ask him where he's been. It's his little secret: he went to have a sauna instead of going to the ball game. So what? It's just his way of having a bit of independence, and it's harmless.

Mr Blue is generally mild-tempered. Life with him is like sailing on a smooth lake in the shimmering sunlight. This does not mean blues are dreary, as many are drawn to the bright lights of showbiz, where they can dazzle. The point is, if your blue lover has managed to hitch his wagon to the stars, then you are fortunate indeed. You'll receive tranquillity with inspiration, plus all the goodies life has to offer. This man above all others has the ability to transform. Somewhere deep in his soul he carries the secrets of the universe. Believe in him, and someday all those dreams of his could come true.

THE BLUE FEMALE

Just got hooked up with a blue-embued female? How fortunate! With her superb clothes and those exquisite liquid big eyes, she is hard to resist – which many a betrayed wife has grieved over. If any female can prize a loyal man away from his spouse it will be her: the divine, kittenish temptress, and so unassuming. Appearing to demand nothing from you other than unadulterated love and romance, nonetheless she somehow always manages to get her trinket box filled before any of her sisters! There won't be many female friends as she is not a lover of her own sex. They are constantly irritated by her manipulative flirting, and why guys can't see what she is up to. Well, they can't. And why should they, when they adore her sweet attention? Once she gets her claws into you, it will be difficult to escape, and you probably won't want to anyway! Who would from a female who is a slave in the kitchen and a enchantress in the bedroom?

She won't want to be the greatest executive in the board-room either; that will be left to her men. Just bring home the goodies and she'll supply the rest. Once she's married she'll set aside the self and her career. A devoted family woman, nothing on earth will stop her from promoting her man or offspring. Her aim is to lure one male only into her domestic den where she'll spin her magical web of ecstasy around him, tying him down forever. Surrender to her cause and you could be in for a delightful time. She'll need constant support and encouragement, hesitating to push forward into the outside world, as she is not naturally competitive. A softie she may appear; nonetheless this lady is not a pushover. Whatever may go wrong for her mate in any area of his life, as far as she is concerned, it will never be his fault. She'll defend your rights to any foe, proving that she does indeed have an iron fist in that velvet glove of hers.

Ms Blue brings wisdom into love. She always gives a promise for tomorrow. Under her quiet exterior lie unfath-omable depths of romance, and ardour. Be assured if she finds she can't please you one way, she'll find another; and, always remain loyal. You are her man and she is your woman, truly believing that for better or worse it will come through for the both of you, just as she always planned it. This lady is all female, dreamy and delightful. She could be a marshmallow ride to heaven.

THE BLUE PARENT

Motherhood suits blue well; in fact, it is a vocation. Blue is the colour of family roots and she never forgets her own childhood. Still waters run deep in this devoted Mother Earth. Possessing a healing voice, she also listens attentively to what her children have to say. She is devoted to her precious darlings from the cradle to the grave to the exclusion of anything else. Through her children she is able to fulfil her own unrequited childhood dreams. The younger generation, animals, and all waifs and strays simply adore Ma Blue. Totally lax with discipline, she is however, extremely ambitious for her family, particularly if they show any talent for the arts or the entertainment world. She can become the stage mother from hell pushing her kids to become stars at all costs.

Pa Blue is inclined to be more laid back. He's still struggling to gain his own maturity! If he's had a success with business it will be easier; if not, then Dad will be preoccupied, with his thoughts elsewhere – the absentee father from pressing circumstances rather than by choice. Education will be a priority and he will go to extreme lengths to provide educational tools, equipment, or extra tuition, in fact whatever is necessary to propel his kids to the fore. When congratulated by others on the splendid performances of his offspring, he will sweetly imply that he has no idea how it happened! It must be down to sheer brilliance on his children's part.

Jealousy and smother love in the teenage years can rear their ugly heads, and create a few ructions, particularly when the children complain of the lack of privacy. It's not that the parents wish to intrude. They do not recognise that the years have passed, and find it hard to accept that their children are not babies any more. On the whole blue parents have the most generous hearts. They are always willing to allay fears and smooth away troubled waters. They are full of compassion, whether their child reaches the heights or becomes a seeming failure or misfit. Ma and Pa Blue will sigh and say 'Never mind darling – stay home with us. It wasn't your fault.' And it never will be, as far as they are concerned.

THE BLUE CHILD

Put on your thinking cap if a bundle of blue joy has just arrived in your household. You will never be able to get the measure of this little cherub's antics. Blue children can run the complete gauntlet of emotions within ten minutes, and then some! Seemingly sweet and docile, you'll find yourself standing at the ready armed with every conceivable appliance, toy and remedy to supply the necessary for this ever-changing, flowing tide of moods. Give up! Let them be; they know what they are doing, and you will never, not ever, be able to be ahead. If your blue kid wants to eat his breakfast under the bed, what the heck! This child is constantly struggling towards a purpose, even if he is not sure what the purpose is. He knew it yesterday, but since then so many avenues have opened up for him that he's just got caught up with the tide.

Blue children are extremely artistic, drawn to sketching and art in particular, so keep them supplied with plenty of paper and paints. When they get a little cranky, just mention the beach; they are fascinated by water creatures, rocks and seashells. Don't mention the two words to them: 'you will'. They'll smile the most delightful, sweet smile, say not a word, and do what they want anyway. These children have the habit of disappearing. Where have they gone this time? Who knows? They'll be back. Let's just hope they haven't buried the cat in the yard, or your latest new hat! Why would they do that? Dunno – but they do! If you want to find out for their safety's sake or for your own sanity, you'll have to stalk them. You'll become the greatest undercover agent of all time.

But look at the plus side. Baby blue has given you, under the guise of parenthood, great training for a future job as a security guard! As blue children have the attention span of a gnat, school can be a problem. They can acquire ace grades, but again it depends on whether they want to or not. A bit reckless with money in their teens, they are inclined to save for ages, and then blow it on a whim. They're suckers for some pretty off-beat causes, so it's best that you keep the key to the piggy bank until they are at least in their fifties!!

From the moment you held baby blue in your arms with her lovely, captivating, lulling quality, you knew you'd never want to let her (or him) go. Together, you can wish upon your own special star in a magical fantasy world.

THE BLUE BOSS

Mr Blue Boss has a touch of the visionary. Just check before you work for him that the money side is in safe hands, which means not in his! He'll make the grade if he has managed to steer himself towards a career that suits him, such as travel or anything to do with entertainment. When this boss becomes bored he dries up, and so will the money. If he can keep the adrenaline going, the finances will flow. He values intellectual integrity and works with a discreet and tactful manner.

Do not be deceived by this boss quietly pondering upon philosophical thoughts – at any moment he can leap into action, surprising all with amazing brilliance when the need arises. Like magicians, blue bosses can pull it out of a hat. Best not to deceive them either; they not only see right through you, but know what you're about to say before you do! Also they are sticklers for the truth – that is, from you – but are themselves inclined to embroider it. 'Isn't that poetic licence?' they will sarcastically retort if challenged. They don't always go by the book and will do anything to avoid confrontation as they abhor arguments. They will resort to manipulation if necessary, reasoning that it makes no difference, as long as the required outcome is the result. They must get their own way, and if you want to keep your job, it's best to button up and go along with them, as basically, at heart, they are tender and caring.

Ms Blue Boss would rather be the power behind the throne instead of out there in the front line. If she does decide to compete in the boardroom, watch out for her persuasive powers. She'll play the vulnerability card to bring out your protectiveness, and before you know it you're hooked; you'll do just about anything for her. She'll gamble on projects where angels would fear to tread. Working for blue power, you'll never know what the day ahead will bring. Let your blue boss know that you are just as daring and scintillating, and are prepared for anything. Keep your suitcase packed, your passport ready. 'Come fly with me,' he or she will call. You should. You won't regret it. The memories will last a lifetime.

THE BLUE EMPLOYEE

The blue employee is a great support for the boss who wants to sound off his ideas. He or she will listen closely to what you have to say, may offer a few sound pieces of advice, even a way out of difficulty with an exceptional idea that has just sprung into their mind – but don't expect them to carry it out for you. You've been given input as far as they are concerned, and you'd better realise the value of it. It doesn't mean that they will do the leg work as well! 'What's that?' you may say. 'Aren't I the boss and you the employee?' Their response will be that they certainly are, but that you can't use them as executives one minute and a shop floor worker the next. It's tricky with the blue employee: there never seem to be any boundaries from which the boss can work.

The nature of these workers is to break down restrictions constantly, because of a deep subconscious desire to set energy free, and a belief that rules and regulations stifle progress. If they become upset they are inclined to let things slide. Although not always loyal to the company – particularly if a better offer comes along – they have the ability while they are with you to make the best of what is. Always doing things their own way, nonetheless they dislike drawing attention to themselves, and will cool and calm all difficult situations. There's a fear of being taken advantage of, as it isn't always easy for them to speak the truth and be heard. They are loners, not needing to hang out with the 'guys', as they are inclined to get bored easily. They will change their job without hesitation if it suits them. They are not too keen on chaos either. If pressurised against their will, they become vague and vacant.

Blues can be an asset to the company, if perhaps a little unconventional and distant, but it certainly makes for an interesting, challenging workplace if they are on a roll! Don't ever underestimate that quiet blue employee sitting in the corner over there. Today a nondescript; tomorrow he or she could be flying to the moon with megabucks! And, they will remember every minute of their time spent with you. How did they get to that position from here? And, seemingly overnight? Aah, there's the secret. It's called poker in the gaming world – keeping your cards close to your chest, taking a chance, and above all ... bluffing!

indigo

THE INDIGO MALE

You are in for a treat if you happen to set your sights on an indigo lover: romance, romance, and more romance. You may quickly come to the conclusion that Mr Right has finally arrived. Watch your step. He may sweep you off your feet, but marriage is another ballgame. Of all the colours, Master Indigo is the trickiest to get to the altar in the first place, and the first to leave when the novelty has worn off.

Check also that you are the only one being wined and dined, and ask how many times he's been married before. Consistency is a slight flaw here! And just when you've made up your mind that this guy is exasperating and you are ready to blow him out, that charming magnetism of his engulfs you, and bingo, you're on again. He's so in love with the chase, that it can blind him to his partner's existence. Two of his irritating faults are arriving late for a date and not hesitating to suggest you leave the theatre or a party early, as he is bored and restless. What he actually means is you've got better things to do than watch this rubbish – but only if you want to go. And you probably will want to, because his seductive voice and gentle touch on your arm, steering you to his romantic hide-away, is irresistible.

Another irritating habit is the way he sizes up every female he meets. He did this with you, as he has to be sure that he is not going to get snared into a situation from which he can't escape. The scenario of being unable to say 'no' to the opposite sex can lead to him being a very unhappy bunny. He won't understand your moods or any subtle hinting from you about your needs, figuring he's not your shrink. It's vital that he makes sure you're going say 'yes' all the way before he makes moves. Decisions are not his forte. Once he's made his mind up to confine you to the rosy love nest, if it suits you, then go for it!

One thing is for sure with this guy: it's all or nothing. Just think. You could be that perfect mate that he has been seeking all his life. Miss Cinderella only needs to pass the last test of fitting that glittering slipper. Squeeze your foot in girl! Do whatever it takes, even if it hurts like mad. You'll soon forget the pain when he spins his honey web, that keeps him in love with you forever.

THE INDIGO FEMALE

An indigo female can see right through you. Although rather moody at times she is, however, basically a drama queen. Her scintillating laugh, along with her strength of spirit, make her a show stopper wherever she goes. The way to win this lady's heart is to act like a man of substance. Lightweight flirts do not interest her. She is a temptress who wants to be taken seriously. Don't be late for a date either, as she is a stickler for punctuality. She is not interested in excuses, such as heavy traffic, or that your best friend has just been admitted to hospital. She expects you to get your priorities right, and that means *her*. You won't be late twice – she'll have taken it that you are not interested in her. You won't want to be late again anyway, because just the thought of catching even a glimpse of her sets your blood racing. She beckons you across plains of experience, both emotional and physical.

Be careful what you say and how you behave around this lady as the merest form of flirting can be misconstrued as a declaration of wedding bell intentions.

Appearing exquisitely dressed – if tending toward a girlie image – she is nonetheless a male thinker. She's smart and will work out all the important decisions in her life logically. Her belief in fair play appeals to the boys, making her a delight in their eyes. She has finely tuned senses, which will be reflected in her fabulous home. It will look like a palace, as she has a natural gift as an interior designer.

When this woman loves it becomes her sole interest. Diplomacy will win her; stupidity and crudeness will not. Once committed, she will never doubt her judgement of choice: total, blind devotion where you are concerned. Nothing will budge her from the love she has for you, so don't let her down. This lady is a femme fatale, with a loyal heart. If she chooses you for her mate, it can only mean that you must be unconventionally rather special too!

THE INDIGO PARENT

Much can be said for the easy-going parenting that children will receive from Mum and Dad Indigo. It will be comfort, comfort all the way. The child will always come first, and the marriage relationship second. The indigo mother can become so devoted to the role of mother and wife that even lying in bed prostrate with illness, she couldn't possibly conceive that anyone else could look after her brood and hold the fort for her. Her aim is to be the epitome of the perfect parent. Keeping a spotless home, the kids will be immaculate too. They will learn the first love of her life was Daddy until they came along, and they will worship her for this. They will also learn that she steers the ship with a strong hand, and as long as they comply with her wishes all will seem cosy, full of love and light. Everyone will know their place, and when all-hands-on-deck is called, they will rise to the signal.

Daddy Indigo, once he has accepted fatherhood, will plunge into the role with enthusiasm. He is not overly keen to participate in everyday practicalities such as feeding junior his puréed berry desert, only to have it flung onto the kitchen floor. It is not a pretty sight, and it depresses him! He'll sigh and look forward to the day when they can become mates, and he can take them hunting, shooting and fishing. Educational trips are right up his street, and the kids will love it, because they will be given the gift of learning through joy. Most indigo parents must be careful not to give their children too full a reign too early, otherwise discipline will be difficult to keep in the teen years. Peace will always be aimed for in the family. The children will not have had to struggle to be heard: free speech will always have been encouraged, with hours having been taken to listen patiently to them. The plus is that they will not push their kids for 'A' grades either. They know it takes more in life than just those. But perhaps it would be wise, as they encourage their darlings to live to the full, to learn that life isn't always fun and games.

These kids will be envied for having such wonderful parents. Other kids will wonder why *theirs* can't be more that way. Childhood memories will certainly be sweet, coupled with fond memories of the special loving guidance they all received in the name of family.

THE INDIGO CHILD

These little darlings of love and light seem like angels in disguise. They are, and will continue to be, as long as you don't hurry or push them. Provide for these delightful cherubs peace, tranquillity, and an ordered routine gently administered, and they will be putty in their parent's hands. Oozing with charisma, they sail easily through childhood bestowing kindness and caring upon all they encounter.

Surely there must be a catch here? Well, yes there is! Part of the charm is just a little smokescreen concealing a desire to get their own way. They like a quiet life and are not unhappy with their own company. 'Own' is a key word in their orbit. It is essential that they are free to do their own thing.

At school they can be unnoticed at first, but when indigo kids come top of the class, consistently, the teacher starts to recognise these budding masterminds. You see, they *do* crave the limelight after all.

Unfortunately, their teenage years can divert them away from their studies more than most. Master and Miss Indigo seem to lose it for a while when they discover the opposite sex. Both ooze this magnetic sexuality and charm. They flirt like mad, constantly on the lookout for a gorgeous specimen of humanity. Don't worry. They come to their senses.

It's best to encourage exercise early on – lazing around is no good for them. Don't listen to their protestations of 'It's too cold', or 'I've got a headache.' After all, didn't they fool you when they were babes in arms? These little dreamboats will always have a few cards hidden up their sleeve. They know from the word 'go' the secrets of success – and the stupidity card is not one of them. These darlings of yours, when dating time arrives, will bring romance back into your life again as they bill and coo over their latest love. It's a joy to behold such sweet trust in the promise of a glorious tomorrow.

To summarise: from birth they have kept their heads down, minded their own business, and when the time was right you witnessed them burst forth and gather up the trophies for which they have worked so hard. They will drink from the cup of life and they won't forget to give you a sip; in fact, they won't forget you at all.

THE INDIGO BOSS

Indigo is a boss with a strong moral sense. He has the ability of being able to plan accurately for the future, transforming and purifying along the way. This boss puts into action what his mouth says. Not easy to work for, he is inclined to become addicted to strict procedures, veering towards fanaticism, and can get stuck in old, traditional patterns. In that indigo bosses possess the unshakeable belief that they are always right, it is important that your ideas coincide with theirs. They are not inclined to take on board your ideas – particularly if they involve get-rich-quick schemes that require cutting corners. It's best to keep these ideas to yourself; or better still, put them on the back burner until you find employment with someone else.

The workplace will be run to order, with nothing left to chance. They make the rules, and if they have embarked into unknown territory where there aren't any, they will set up a mini-establishment which must adhere to the law. They always flourish in positions of authority.

The only areas of employment they themselves would consider would be the law, where a position as a judge would suit, as the legal profession intrigues them. Perfect justice is their aim in all their endeavours. They have a unique gift of being able to listen to and tease everyone's opinions out into the open, laying all the options bare to be dissected. They are also great mediators, piecing everything together.

Indigos bask in teamwork – the Lone Ranger style of working is not for them. If you want to win their favour, be totally up-front. Scheming is their prerogative, not yours!

On a good day, both male and female indigos are right little charmers. The indigo she-boss has no hesitation in putting herself about to get the desired results. Mr Indigo can turn the schmaltz on like a tap if it suits him. He can also turn it off just as fast. This boss will never become your mate, but treated fairly you will be. Working for them can be a joy, and so interesting, as they always have something new in preparation. An air of expectancy continually pervades the atmosphere. Indigo can combine both worlds – creativity and materialism – and provide a constancy of work and security, along with play and inspiration.

THE INDIGO EMPLOYEE

Indigos work like bloodhounds. Once given the scent, they track down every possible lead, while following the boss's instructions to the letter. This is definitely a power worker behind the throne, but one who still finds time for the rest of the team. Above all Mr or Ms Indigo employees want to be proud of their boss, but at the same time they also need to be recognised for their contribution to the company. Both male and female indigos bring balance and harmony to the office. They give the impression of being creative but of being somewhat disinterested regarding ideas under discussion. They may seem to contribute very little to the latest project, when suddenly, out comes the dazzling solution which is sheer genius. These are all or nothing employees. You'll just have to treat them as hot-house flowers, even veer towards pampering them – although it may stick in your throat.

Liken their patterning to that of the rare tulip tree, which blossoms only once every 15 years. When it does, it is spec-tacular. It develops steadily – just like your indigo employees – for a long time, and eventually bursts forth into breathtaking blossoms which put everything else into the shade. A moment in time has been created! Just be patient and they'll come up with it again! Take a gamble; it's rather exciting, knowing that the pot of gold at the end of the rainbow is bound to overflow at any moment.

Indigos appreciate harmonious surroundings where they can rest a little, although you may argue that they have to work, not dream. The system has been purposely set up by them this way so that no one else can operate it. Smart, you may say. And why not? You hired them for their brains didn't you? You also realised their unconventionality too, didn't you?

When you have indigo employees, they take care of them-selves by making themselves indispensable. They may have their quirky ways of filing and fulfilling their role, but who cares, because whichever way they go about their assignments the work gets done, and won't cause you, the boss, any hassle. They possess indigo's energy, and as part of a workforce their motto will be: 'I'll do it boss, whatever it takes.' Trust me.

purple

THE PURPLE MALE

The purple lover tends to play a leading role in the community, a man who can make you dizzy with his seductive power. He knows that there is no greater aphrodisiac to attract a woman than a male who commands respect wherever he goes. Being recognised as his lady means his accomplishments rub off on you, making you special in other people's eyes and resulting in VIP treatment. But before he bestows this honour on you, you will be tested first. This man likes to savour the challenge that ensues – it will be more like an obstacle course for you, where you will be expected to surmount each hurdle, passing with flying colours. Don't make it easy for him either, as he respects a woman who values herself. Once he is convinced you are the one, he will send the most divine love letters and poetry. Now that you've proved your worth, he'll treat you gently and kindly from now on, even handling you with kid gloves.

To keep this male, you must remain self-assured, as he needs to admire you. He adores basking in the envy of other males as they view his special arm-candy, which is you! Master Purple does not play around, as he is addicted to an ideal of love – which can prove to be totally unrealistic. At a glance he can tell a quality lady, which leads him to become a bit of a loner, as he will not waste time with crowds of mediocraties searching for her. He knows she won't be hanging out with the gang. But he can become moody at times, as he has a very suspicious nature. Once he decides you are the one he will pursue you ardently with love, propelling you into realms of delight and happiness, reckoning that you are worth it. It will only ever be the best that will be good enough for you both.

As the purple male is fascinated by the mystic arts, he reaches up to the higher planes of consciousness and knowledge. He aims for perfection of union both physically and spiritually. He can make your inner candle burn brightly. As purple is made up of red and blue, the cool energy of blue will give him an air of stability, and the red will show an extreme talent for sexual love. He becomes a passionate man, but with brains as well. This man resides in the heart of the universe. You will have been tested as an initiate on the secrets of life and all-consuming passion. Having passed with honours, he will be yours in that inner sanctum of infinite love. He is truly a man to die for.

THE PURPLE FEMALE

This lady has great poise, and is a possessor of hidden qualities of understanding which allow her to be the great humanitarian. A woman of substance, she will not waste her time on low levels of emotion. With her you'll encounter a breadth of experience, wrapped up in a package of gentleness, tied with a string of kindness. She initially appears demanding because this time around on the planet, she is a leader. But while she pushes herself, she also guides you in the right direction, which can be a plus, enabling you to reach your goals. This lady will not keep you dangling on a string, as she either likes or dislikes you instantly. Indeed she is a mysterious beauty who can send shivers of heady delight tingling up and down your spine. But she is not a lady who will manipulate her way into your affections. She knows that one whiff of her exotic perfume will make you come running anyway. Even the lowering of those sexy eyelids will capture your heart. And her clothes will be alluring. Preferring men's company, her aim is to get you, the male. Nothing will dissuade her once she puts her plan into action.

Somehow the purple female has an uncanny understanding of the opposite sex, so you had better be honest with her. Don't even dare to think of fooling around with someone else if you have indicated your interest in her exclusively. You will truly regret taking advantage of her advances.

Think twice, or maybe even three times, before embarking upon a lifetime partnership with this lady. Once you're ensnared, she'll never let you go, regardless of what you've done, or even if you feel it's time for you to move on. You are hers, and she'd rather see you off this planet than allow you to walk out on her. Nobody, but nobody, leaves once she has made a commitment and you agree to it. If it's another woman you're going to, then hide her away. If Mrs Purple gets to her, it won't be a pretty sight.

Cool, enticing, secretive, even dangerous – this lady is a handful. You're playing with fire, but boy is it worth it! This lady knows her own mind, and probably yours as well. A strong, passionate sex bomb, or a sweet, gentle sweetheart, she's all yours. Never weak or needy, she'll allow you to dominate her – but only on her terms. It's all or nothing with Ms Purple lover. If she has chosen you, then your lucky number has come up! You've definitely won the lottery of love.

THE PURPLE PARENT

Great teachers for their children, purple parents will not allow them to waste time, encouraging them to sample an enormous variety of interests. Every avenue must be explored, both at home and at school. Mr and Mrs Purple both put an enormous amount of energy into their partners and their children. Joint pursuits are what this ship is run on. Mother feels it's essential for father to participate in their upbringing; you can't leave her at home alone with the kids for too long. It's best, really, if she has boys, as she can't be bothered with girlish frills. A strong mother, she encourages her offspring to achieve by giving them enormous shoves.

She also supports them while they move through their fears, and the children gain confidence just by watching her. In no way will anyone be allowed to cause her child any problems – they will be wiped out. She may not pander to her children, but heaven help those who dare to threaten her brood. Dad can appear to be harsh with discipline, but Mum will definitely keep an eye on this.

A lot of intense, bossy energy will be generated within the family, and life at home will be extremely hectic, with not a dull moment. The household will be run on masculine principles. Even mother loves to rough and tumble with the kids, relishing any adventurous outdoor pursuits.

Much as these parents keep their children hard at it, they also reward well and acknowledge any achievement. Provided these parents are in a positive mood, all will be well. It's hard for them to concede that sometimes their kids may feel down, or just need a little quiet space to recoup. They also need to remember that not everyone has the same dynamism and curiosity as they do. Even when they do realise, they can still fall into the trap of urging and pushing for action, when contraction would be more appropriate at that time.

All this said, these parents are basically an inspiration to their young. They weave magic and mystery into all forms of learning, so that the child becomes spell-bound by the wonders of the universe. A great plus of having a purple parent is that come what may, loyalty is the name of the game. Through all of life's trials and tribulations ultimately you are their child, and burning coals will never stop them from seeing to your welfare first.

THE PURPLE CHILD

Well now, if baby purple has just arrived on the scene, you could get lulled into thinking that this quiet little being will be a piece of cake. How wrong, you realise a while later. How is it the whole house, including you, revolves around these children, and they don't even seem to holler? Look into their eyes and you will see deep wells of subtle knowledge. They seem to have been born old, with a sorcerer's mystic understanding that hypnotises you. They are intense and heavyweights in the emotional area. Do what they want. Do what they want and they will be your slave – or is it you who is the slave? Does it matter? When all runs smoothly in the nursery you have here a relationship between baby and parent that surpasses all expectations of joy. Disturb your diddums space and you will wish you'd never been born, let alone become a parent!

Miss Purple takes well to being a tomboy as a child; that's why in her teens and as an adult she is so good with the guys – she just knows how a male ticks. From an early age she figures out that boys have the edge, that society favours them, so if you can't beat 'em, join 'em!

Master Purple never appears to act like a child, possessing a wise head on his young shoulders. If you pay attention, you'll cotton on fast that this Prince Charming is the boss – it's as simple as that.

At school and college they have to be kept busy. Immensely inquiring and energetic in mind and body, they need to be stretched continually. Inclined to be moody, they need to be encouraged to move beyond themselves. You may not be able to penetrate deeply into their thoughts, as they are secretive. Just offer kind, gentle words, and explain to them the reason why it may be a good idea to come back to earth, and make up their minds to participate in the land of the living.

These children are mediators; they have the ability to access all realms of consciousness. They may get their fingers burnt a few times, and so will you when they challenge your authority. One thing is for sure – if you keep the home fires burning brightly, they'll always return to you to warm themselves by its glowing embers.

THE PURPLE BOSS

All purple bosses are a law unto themselves. Basically, they can only be self-employed – they are the leaders, the masters, capable of great rulership. They command respect despite being overbearing and avid social climbers. These bosses have a goal in mind and will achieve it come what may. Their tactics may not always be fair, they may even be ruthless and corrupt, but they do not let their emotions govern their business activities. Lovers of power for its own sake, they are the conquerors. You'll never know whether their sting is worse than their bite! Acquire some protective emotional armour when you work for these true power-houses. They are not easy people to work for – even appearing harsh at times – but possessing inspiration, personality, and a surprising grasp of universal consciousness. The red in purple enables them to surmount any obstacles; the blue in purple causes them to pause and think before they journey down any unusual avenues. They can be found in all areas of business.

The purple boss is pretty exciting to work for: a tower of strength and forcefulness, coupled with the unexpected and the unknown. A regular roller-coaster of events and happenings will be constantly challenging for any employee. Sometimes this boss will throw a spanner in the works just to keep you on your toes. It's mean, but when you're congratulated afterwards on your expertise, you will be secretly pleased that you have risen to the challenge. His kindness, when it comes to the fore, will never be mistaken for weakness, so don't think you can take advantage. If you think you can flutter your eyelashes or waffle your way out of any situation with this boss, forget it! He'll never be tempted or side-tracked from the project at hand. If you've messed up, it's best to come clean. When he knows how you've tried with good intentions, he'll let you off the hook. Fouling up because you were careless means you've just blown your job away. You'll know this by the way a quiet disinterest appears on his face. You don't exist. Best to resign – it'll be less painful for you. The purple emperor expects high standards from you – as, indeed, he does from himself.

A boss royal he may be, but he is still intoxicating to work for, an outstanding combination of practical ability, coupled with idealism. If you're ambitious clamber onto his bandwagon, he'll take care of the lows so you can hit the highs together.

THE PURPLE EMPLOYEE

Purple employees seek a boss who is socially connected. They always check first that where they are working will get them invited to influential places. They make very good business partners, particularly for a company of high standing and flair. Of course, it's only a matter of time before they decide to run their own company. You can give them a project and leave them with it. By the time the board meeting has assembled they will be ready, having sewn up every possible avenue for the advantage of the company. But don't expect them to come up with on-the-spot, quick answers. They prefer to mull over their strategy in private, which will be fool-proof by the time the action goes into play. They always need to be at the core of decision making, always liking to think at the executive level of business. No lightweights, they want to be taken seriously. Never treat them as insignificant run-arounds, otherwise you may find that when they leave you, they've run off with contacts, taking your business with them.

They are masters of their destiny, only employed on their own terms. Wherever they work, they know exactly what they are doing, and why. It may be a little harder for you, the boss, to know! They keep tricks of the trade and how they do it close to their chest – a guarded secret.

Purple employees are excellent in money markets; looking to the future, they always invest shrewdly. They are always able to squeeze the best possible deal from any business project. You cannot fault them with their mastery of detail: they know every angle and have a marvellous touch for negotiating.

It is impossible for them not to promote an image. Even if a purple employee is the porter of a hotel, it will be the most exclusive, of course. You'll wonder for just a second if he is the owner! Above all else, as employees they know that he who pays the piper calls the tune. They may appear to be behind the scenes, but it's only a respite while they compose their own song. They never give the boss short change, so it's best if they are not abused. Long after they have gone, they never forget how good you were to them while they were climbing up the rungs of that ladder leading to success.

9

mystic colour

Divination and Colour

Divination is the predicting or indicating of future events by methods and means of seeing that are beyond the usual senses. It can likewise be used for looking backwards. We can acknowledge it as an intuitive sense, with its own rationality. It is available to any and all who can trust in other than what is seen by the naked eye. It has been called a gift from the gods, coming from the air that surrounds us. When it is used in its purity to receive answers to questions, problems, or general information that can give us an edge, it enhances and benefits mankind, bringing comfort for those in need, and solace where there is unrest. It's all a matter of moving the self into a deeper consciousness of total awareness.

Psychic ability is something that we all have to a certain degree, as inherent as your sight or sense of smell. Colour is part and parcel of the psychic makeup of human beings.

Colour is a *psychic* sense. It is important to understand that being 'psychic' is a natural talent of the human body/mind, not something mysterious and out-of-this-world. However, as with colour, it is a talent nobody ever taught us to develop or make use of, far less trust and embrace. It is the ability to fine tune the senses. It can be achieved by simply making your-self available and clear of mind, so that which is always there can be picked up. Students can prepare themselves with the aid of colour. Colour is part of your physic make-up, and it helps to connect you to your physic space.

Before delving into specific techniques of divination, it is necessary to discover your soul essence, that unseen part of you that has the ability to gain knowledge from the unseen realm of understanding.

Soul Colour

Your soul is the foundation of everything that occurs in this life – and others. The soul is the very essence of you person-ally, the core substance. It is pure undiluted spirit. It is not the same as karma. Karma is the pattern of actions taken, or not taken, by the individual bodies the soul has inhabited while on Earth. Karma is constantly changing by actions – the soul remains constant no matter what does or doesn't happen to the personalities it has occupied.

The colour of the soul is considered by most seers to be blue while it inhabits the body; it reverts back to the clear brilliance upon death. The soul colour turns into other colours, or shades of grey or black when wrong ways of think-ing and conduct threaten its purity; when its bearer has lost the pathway of right living. Being in the blue is the goal. It is man's trial throughout life to keep it this colour, the soul connection to the heavens above.

Working with your colour and resolving its negativity will bring that colour's vibration back to normality. We all have the seven colours of the spectrum in equal amounts within our system. The aim is to keep it that way, so that our soul can retain its blue hue, enabling us to conduct ourselves with decency, honour and integrity on a daily basis.

DISCOVERING YOUR PERSONAL SOUL COLOUR

An easy way to discover your soul colour is to meditate on the breath, which opens a channel of cosmic communication.

1 Sit or lie, and relax. Focus on your breath coming in and going out for 11 breaths.

2 Become aware of that space you enter before a breath is taken in or expelled out. It is a kind of 'U-turn' before the beginning or the ending of either of these actions.

3 Stay in this 'U-turn' space for a while each time. While there, allow yourself to explore and go 'walkabout'.

4 After a few cycles, look for a colour in your next 'U-turn' space.

5 Remember this colour.

6 When you're ready open your eyes, and allow your personal celestial colour to flash before your eyes for instant attunement. This is the perfect key colour for you to tune in to, or meditate with for a while, before beginning any form of personal-growth work.

LIGHT ABSORPTION: THE BRILLIANCE

This is a developmental process as a preparation for the divination exercises in the remainder of the chapter. This process can also be done on a daily basis to heighten your awareness of colour as a tool.

Seers have always used the brilliance (see page 150) to

foretell the future, whether gazing into a pond or a glass of clear water or a crystal ball. People often ask me how I get answers for questions. I reply, 'Use the light and it will tell you.' To be able to see anything, you have to gaze into a clear space. A simple process to help you start your development along these lines is an absorption of the light technique. It is a fascinating way of training yourself to become sensitive to the brilliance. The method is as follows:

◆ Look into an electric bulb and stare without blinking for 30 seconds (not longer than this).
◆ Immediately close your eyes and see where it leads you.
◆ Look at the pictures, shapes, colours, and so on, that have come through to you.

This is a very positive way to start training your psychic powers by working with the light.

◆ **A word of caution – *do not* use this process by looking into the sun, as severe eye damage will result. Only use an electric light bulb.**

TAKING STOCK:
THE COLOUR RELATE READING

This is a way of giving yourself a colour reading. Just follow the instructions and go with your intuition. You can also use the colour interpretative materials in Chapter 7 to help you with your analysis. This reading gives you information on earthly, mundane issues, and it also brings in your divinitive qualities. It gets to the core of the matter by exposing fruitless behaviour patterns, and it allows the inner mind to become flexible. Using colour gives as clear an association with the truth as possible. When a colour is selected, it is an indication of the internal patterns that ultimately affect us on the outside. Colour enables us to communicate with the hidden parts of ourselves, and helps us to uncover our own, sometimes hidden, agendas.

If a satisfying career seems to elude you, or if you can't understand why life doesn't work out for you, a colour relate reading can help you. You have the information resources in The Psychology of Colour chapter, all you need now is the method, and to tune into your intuition to help you with your analysis.

Your reading is given by having a selection of coloured cards which you can easily make at home. First, make seven cards a single hue – the seven spectrum colours; for others draw a line across the centre of the card, with the top half one colour and the bottom half another. Be sure your two-colour cards include all the seven colours of the spectrum, as well as the shades, tints and combinations listed in Chapter 7, if possible. The more colours available, the wider the reading.

When the two-colour cards are chosen in the reading, the top section represents concious thoughts, and the action to be taken. The lower half represents subconcious thoughts, or what you would like to happen but as of yet has not taken place.

Preparation

First shuffle your pack of colour cards. Spread the cards on the table before you in a semi-circle. When you spread the cards, keep them in the same upright position they are in the deck; this determines which is the 'top' colour and which is the 'bottom' colour. It is always a good idea to keep a pad and pencil nearby, so that notes can be recorded.

Method

Ten colours will be chosen by you – or the person for whom you are reading if you are not reading for yourself. These are

Colour relate reading

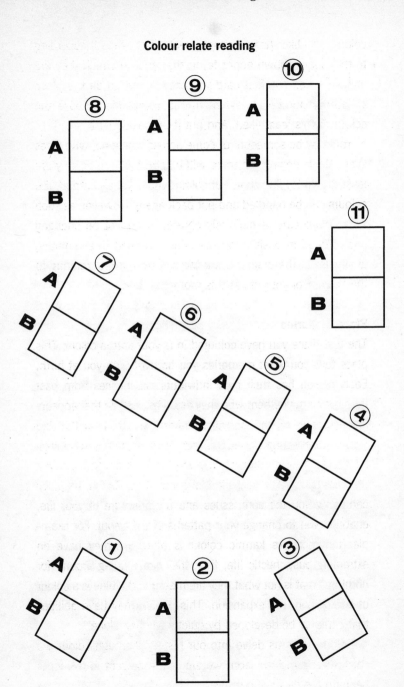

colours you like. As you choose each card, place it according to the layout shown opposite, in the order in which they are chosen – i.e., the first card you choose will go on the place of karma, number 1. When this is completed, choose the colour that is least liked, and put it on position 11.

You may be someone, or come across someone, who loves every single colour, but there will be one that you or they are least drawn to. The choice of colours must not be hurried, the colours can be handled and put back again. However, as soon as a colour card is definitely chosen, it cannot be changed once placed in position on the table. The first three colours, as shown in the diagram, are the 'set up' places, relating to the 'set up' of your life at this moment.

Place 1: Karma

The first place you have coloured in is your karma colour. This place tells you what memories you brought with you at birth. Each person has their own individual experiences from past lives which make them who they are. The past life that appears simply shows up the everyday patterns of behaviour that the person is struggling with in this lifetime. It is an important place as it gives an indication of why you live your life the way you do, and in turn why your life is the way it is. The karma place can show you the core issues and the structure of your life, enabling you to change your patterns of behaviour. For example, if a person's karmic colour is blue and they have an extremely busy, hectic life, then they are running around for nothing – that is not what they are meant to do: blue is a colour of contraction, not expansion. This person may have abilities that can *only* be developed by quietly working alone.

Colour helps us delve into our history. Through colour we can move from the bloom we are in the present to the roots beneath the earth of our past.

Whenever I ask someone what they understand karma to be they usually reply 'cause and effect'. Well, what does that mean? Does it mean that if I've been good before in previous lives I will have a good life now this time round? If I have been bad will I only receive bad things in this life?

I personally do not believe that what happens to you in this lifetime is a punishment for what you did before, but you will bring in with you from birth your own personal sum and substance from past lives, which is unique to you and is the blueprint for the learning that comes with you from your past.

Place 2: Childhood
The second place tells us what you were doing as a child. This colour tells you how you felt at home and how you perceived the world to be.

Place 3: Today
The third place tells you where you are today, right now, this minute. This is useful as it can show whether you are preparing for the future ahead.

Next 7 Places: Insight Colours
That which is coming in
The next seven colour places, numbers 4–10, indicate what is coming in for the next seven years. Each place is a year. If you wish to go beyond seven years just add more colour cards. Use the colour interpretations in Chapter 7. Which interpretation applies, and *how* the interpretation applies, comes from your own intuition.

Aspects of what you see in one year may run into other years. If you have used a two-colour card, you read the line in the middle of the card as a division between the body above the waist (A) and below (B) in the physical body, and between the conscious (A) and subconscious (B) in the mental and spiritual realm. In other words, A shows us what you are consciously doing in life, and B is what you might like to do. If you use a single-colour card you are working on the same aspects consciously and subconsciously.

Never forget that colours have many meanings. You will know intuitively when you read the interpretative chapter what the colours mean for you. For instance, your combination may be yellow (A) with mid-blue (B) which for you may mean that you need to think through (blue) your actions (yellow) – or, it's about time you thought before you acted.

Disliked Colour Place – Hindrance

The disliked colour needs to be looked at closely. It shows what could hinder and cause disruption at some point during the next seven-year period. It is a very important placing. This is card number 11, a master number. It symbolises your ability to get to grips with your negative patterning. Do so, and the advancement in your life will be tremendous. Number 11, broken down, becomes the number 2, the number of perfect peace and harmony – relating to the colour green. Taking note and acting on this card's information could turn around any adversity and disappointment, opening the way for positive growth. For example, if you dislike indigo, it could be saying that there is a need to structure your life better and in more detail. Careless planning will not do – it is best not the leave things to chance.

Hidden Colours

Some colours are combinations of other colours, so if you find the information not forthcoming with a chosen colour, you can read it on the hidden level only. Take into account all unseen colours – they will give valuable insight. For example, when purple is chosen, do not ignore the hidden red and blue that is in it. Colours with hidden components, to be taken into account if an obvious answer is not forthcoming, are:

◆ Orange: hidden yellow and red
◆ Green: hidden blue and yellow
◆ Purple: hidden red and blue
◆ Turquoise: hidden green, blue and yellow

Unchosen Colours

During a reading one or more of the seven spectrum colours are often omitted. The left out colours show where the deepest challenges lie over the next seven-year period. Orange is often the most rejected colour. A dislike of orange shows a fear of moving forward, which an infusion of red will rectify by giving a short sharp push into activity.

Colour Rejection

It is very rare for an individual to say that they do not like colour of any kind, but it happens. A person who spurns colour by positively avoiding it reveals a deep need for comfort: somewhere in their lives they were pained emotionally to such an extent that they pushed away the light. This person will need gentle persuasion to join the human race again, as confidence and trust has been lost. An exposure to soft pink will help by giving a consistency of comfort.

INSTANT COLOUR CHECK

Everyone has three colours that influence them and will be around them in several areas in their everyday life. There may be a strong second colour, or even a third. But there is always a dominant colour. My dominant colour is red. But I often work from a very strong yellow influence, and sometimes purple.

Once you discover what colour light you are working with, you will understand better your relationships with others, work and life. The next question, of course, is: how do I find out what my three colours are?

To do this instant colour check, write down on a piece of paper the first three colours that come into your mind. It helps to draw three circles and colour them in. Label them in the order that they appear to you. The first is your personality colour; the second is your work colour and will show your creative abilities. This is the colour to surround yourself with at work as much as possible as it will support you in your endeavours. The third will be your social colour and show how you interact with other people and the world. It is the colour that motivates you in relationships in every area.

By reading The Psychology of Colour chapter, and the Life's Colours chapter, you may find that you have a feeling, an inclination, an understanding about these colours.

When you know your three colours, you can use them to recharge your batteries. A few minutes' meditation on your three colours does more to strengthen your system and constitution than any other booster programme. For instance, if your personal colour is blue, why not put blue sheets on your bed. If your work colour is orange, why not choose this shade for your desk equipment and stationery. And if your social colour is yellow, then wear yellow clothes at parties, at work, or even when you go shopping. If in doubt at any point, use white.

Check to see how your three colours interact with each other. For instance, if your personality colour is purple and your social colour is yellow your personality has a good chance of attracting the relationships it wants. But if your personality is red and your social colour is orange there may be friction between the two and your personality may find it difficult to get on with people.

Further Colour Techniques for Divination

DOWSING THE COLOUR WHEELS

A good technique for accessing your intuitiveness is through the use of a pendulum with a colour wheel. All you need to begin is a piece of white paper and a pendulum.

The Pendulum

A clear crystal pendulum is best, but alternatively, a clear glass bead or button tied at the end of a piece of thread also works. Hold the end of the thread between the first finger and thumb so that the crystal or button hangs down, and place it over the colour wheel (how to make this is explained below). Then, ask it a question. Only ask one question at a time to be clear about where the answer applies. Remember, the pendulum is an extension of you, and it is really the deeper, intuitive part of yourself that is reflected in its motion.

The Colour Wheels

1 THE FULL-SPECTRUM COLOUR WHEEL

1 On your piece of white paper, draw a circle several inches in diameter. Divide the circle into seven pie-shaped sections. Colour each section a spectrum colour, one of the seven hues.

2 Use a clear pendulum when working with the full-spectrum wheel. For general guidance, place your pendulum in the centre of the colour wheel, and ask your question.

3 Allow your pendulum to swing freely until it moves over to a colour-segment – or not. If it does not move to a colour segment and the question requires a 'yes' or 'no' answer,

the answer is 'no'. If it moves to a coloured segment, the answer is 'yes', and by going to the colour interpretations in Chapter 7, you allow your intuition to guide you while interpreting the colour shown. For example, if you have asked 'Should I go out tonight?' and the pendulum moves to blue, the answer is 'yes', but the blue segment indicates 'proceed with caution'. It won't be a wild night out. However, if it moves to orange, then it means 'party time ahead!' – a successful social event.

2 THE SINGLE-COLOUR WHEEL
Specific Area Answers

You may also wish to focus on specific areas such as children or your sex-life, both of which, as you'll discover from the list below, relate to red. To give added potency to the single-colour wheel, you can use pendulums with crystals or buttons the same colour as the life area for which you are seeking answers, as listed below.

1 In The Psychology of Colour chapter, check for the number of combinations, shades and tints of red that are listed. Construct a colour wheel as described previously, but using only these variations of red.

2 Use the pendulum as before, to see which red it moves towards. Consult the colour interpretations, as before with the spectrum wheel. If it stops over pale pink, for example, there is a need for affection rather than a passionate love life at the moment, a need for protection and security. If it stops over dark red, it shows your relationships are stale, and you could be bullied by the opposite sex. Bright red will show that you are now ready to progress fully in life, your spirits are high, your blood is up, and at this moment it's a good time to push projects forward.

You can construct charts for any colour areas you wish. Use the list below for direction on which colour to use.

LIFE AREAS RELATING TO SPECIFIC COLOURS

◆ **Red:** journeys, sexual attractions, family, life empowerment
◆ **Orange:** work, career opportunities, divorce, freedom
◆ **Yellow:** agility of mind, study, communication, the media
◆ **Green:** money, business stability, marriage, good health, romance
◆ **Blue:** acceptance of peace, the healer, literary accomplishment, truth seeker
◆ **Indigo:** fortitude, indispensability, house moves, psychic potential, constructiveness
◆ **Purple:** leadership qualities, artistic talent, self-employment, inventiveness

Scrying

CRYSTAL BALL COLOURS

The word scrying means 'seeing'. It is divination – seeking the future – by peering into any reflective surface such as water, mirrors, or crystals, in which are formed visions, symbols or pictures. At some point virtually every culture has employed methods of divination for scrying, particularly when there were worries about the future.

COLOURED SEEING

The reason for the popularity of crystal-ball gazing has always been its simplicity. Working with the crystal ball's reflections, you are engaging the brilliant light from whence all colours come – giving a glimpse into the infinity of invisible light, wherein are contained all things. Crystal-ball gazing is much easier than the elaborate rituals that other means of divination sometimes require. A quartz crystal ball has always been a favourite tool of clairvoyants and seers.

Beryl, of which emerald and aquamarine are variants, was a favourite with wealthy scryers of the past. You can use these today if you wish – if you can afford a piece the size of an orange! Beryl is usually tinted green, which, of course, will influence the reading. The green will bring the ball's focus onto new beginnings and happenings, such as business projects and new romances which are imminent, rather than events likely to happen years hence.

Dr Dee, court astrologer to Queen Elizabeth I of England, used a black Mexican obsidian ball the size of an egg. Her Majesty would make no important decision without first consulting her personal screer. In 1696, the famous seer John Aubrey advised that a ball used for divination should have a tint of red, thought to quicken happenings and speed up events. This colour encouraged 'pictures in the fire to be seen', similar to staring into the embers of a glowing fire, which was another favourite, common method of divination. It was believed among early scryers that the stronger the colour of the ball, the more the events foreseen in them were likely to be hastened. But black or colourless balls were only thought to span backwards and forwards in time, without exerting any influence on events that would take place in the future.

Scrying is a valid and active way of developing your own clairvoyant abilities. All that enters its realm will be recorded and shown back to you ... so let's begin:

EQUIPMENT
◆ For basic scrying, all you need is a clear crystal ball made of glass or quartz, with a stand to stop the ball from rolling around.

◆ Stands of natural substances such as brass or wood are best.

◆ If you don't have a crystal ball, a glass or bowl of water, a mirror, or any reflective surface will substitute. You can even stare into a pond, a lake, or even a puddle.

◆ If you are not staring into a pond or lake, you will also need a table on which to put the ball or other scrying object.

◆ Use a black cloth to cover the table (although a white cloth can be used when using a coloured ball).

◆ If you are using a coloured crystal, be aware that the colour's vibration will influence the energy coming through, skewing the reading towards the life area represented by the colour. You can also use this tendency of the coloured crystal to focus deliberately on a specific area, such as using a yellow crystal ball to see if you are likely to pass an exam, or for career possibilities. If you choose this method, and cannot afford a selection of different-coloured balls, keep a number of coloured cloths handy, which can be placed under a clear crystal to colour it. For the colours associated with various life-areas, consult the list on page 324.

◆ Never allow anyone else to touch or handle your scrying equipment.

◆ Always wrap the crystal ball in black or purple velvet after use, and put it safely away in a dark-coloured box, in a drawer.

A PLACE TO WORK

◆ You need a place to work where it is quiet and uncluttered.

◆ Keep the room and all equipment spotlessly clean: dust hinders physic phenomena.

◆ If the room is to be darkened, two candles can be used – preferably white in brass holders.

◆ You will also need two chairs: one for the seer and one for the sitter.

◆ More than one person present for a sitting is generally not recommended, but an exception can be made for one person to act as a support for the sitter if they feel they would be more comfortable – as long as they do not interrupt the session.

WHEN TO WORK

◆ The traditional, and best, time to work is when the moon is waxing. Scrying works best when the sun is at its farthest northern position; but, provided the body is relaxed and the nerves are calm to allow concentration, readings can be done at any time.

◆ Visualise gold to steady the psyche, and to encourage a successful reading.

DON'T!

◆ ... try placing the crystal ball into circles on the floor or onto so-called 'holy tables' – that's if you can even get one! These involve elaborate rituals and are definitely not for the beginner or amateur.

◆ ... work with a smoky quartz crystal. Its brown colour will not allow you to penetrate, delaying and distorting the reading ... and leads to disappointment.

PREPARATION

◆ You are the only person who should handle your crystal ball.

◆ To prepare it for work, cleanse, by gently washing it in a little white vinegar and tepid water. Then polish it dry with a velvet cloth or chamois leather.

◆ Never expose your crystal ball to extreme temperatures.

◆ Do not expose it to direct sunlight.

◆ Moonlight is beneficial.

◆ A dimly lit room is required.

◆ It is best that the sitter is opposite you.

◆ It is easier to put the ball on a stand freeing both hands; but it can be held in the palm of your hand if no table is available.

SEEING PICTURES

◆ Don't worry if you are unable to see anything at first. Scrying comes easily to only one person in twenty. Practice and perseverance will help to develop any latent powers.

◆ When staring into a crystal or the chosen reflector, it is usual initially to see a milky-white hue. Allow the mist to transform and take shape to reveal shapes, symbols, or sometimes even pictures.

◆ It's rare to get whole scenes or pictures immediately, only the gifted psychic will do so, but a misty impression is often all that is needed to lead into an interpretation.

◆ You may be able to get insights and clues only in black and white, and grey clouding. Be patient and stay with it. These can turn into colour impressions, giving further guidance for interpretation.

Many images or impressions you receive will be self-explanatory. The basic images of coloured clouding which often appear are explained opposite, enabling you to read and interpret their messages.

BLACK AND WHITE CLOUDS

◆ Black and white are usually the first colours to be seen by the beginner scryer.

◆ White clouds are indicators of peace and contentment;

black clouds are often signs of trouble ahead, a time to take extra care.

◆ With practice you will eventually pass through this blurred stage to find meanings in the mist.

COLOURED CLOUDS
Red, Orange and Yellow Clouds

◆ When these colours are seen, a lot of energy will be needed for endeavours to come to pass.

◆ It is wise to think before you leap into any new situation.

◆ These are signs of movement and action – not static.

◆ Good health is indicated.

Green Clouds

◆ Money prospects are stable. Prosperity coming in.

◆ Pay close attention to relationships and encourage the growth of love.

◆ It is a contented time for the home and family.

Blue, Indigo and Purple Clouds

◆ These point out that it is time to reconsider and restructure one's life in a positive manner. Tidy up loose ends.

◆ You can obtain all that is desired, but only if careful planning is followed.

◆ It is possible to get stuck in a rut if you are not careful.

◆ Peace should not be attained at any price.

MOVING CLOUDS
Ascending Clouds

◆ Yes to all questions.

◆ Red, orange and yellow – foretell extreme activity; positive indicators.

◆ Green – life looks good; stable situations.

◆ Blue, indigo and purple – take the lead; you have the necessary wisdom and experience; it is a good time to be self employed.

Descending Clouds
◆ No to all questions.
◆ Red, orange and yellow – you are neglectful and slap-dash in something important; your lofty standing may take a long fall; closure to a project is imminent.
◆ Green – money is going out faster than it is coming in/wasteful.
◆ Blue, indigo and purple – disappointment and loss of opportunities; beware delusions of grandeur/pomposity.

Clouds Moving to the Right
◆ A good omen. Beneficial support is at hand.
◆ Red, orange and yellow – results will soon be forthcoming.
◆ Green – a comfortable period; a good time to borrow money.
◆ Blue, indigo and purple – stand up and be recognised; your time has come.

Clouds Moving to the Left
◆ A period of positive energy is coming to an end.
◆ Red, orange and yellow – you have just missed the boat; the opportunity is gone; cancellations of important matters.
◆ Green – your money is rapidly running out; there is jealousy about you/underhandedness.
◆ Blue, indigo and purple – this is definitely not the time to push forward or ask for promotion.

Colour Your Dreams

In ancient times dreams played a very important role in human affairs, assuming far greater significance than now. The earliest written records of dreams were found in an Egyptian papyrus from around 1250 BC. In it, priests of the falcon-headed god Horus described over 200 dreams and their interpretations. To obtain a cure by dream contact with a healing god was necessary. To obtain divine advice through a dream was accomplished by sleeping in a temple. This sleeping period was known as an 'incubation period'. The dreams thus experienced brought an awareness of constant contact with a mysterious supernatural world, from which might be learned one's own destiny in this world and the next.

Dreams can reveal the deepest levels of personal existence. Have you ever wondered where the light comes from to illuminate your dreams? You are sound asleep in a dark room with your eyes shut, yet something is stimulating the light! In the black there is eternal light, springing forth in the dark secret place of the womb. Your body of light was always with you – your dreams are the proof of that.

Psychoanalysts attach significance to dreams, but beyond this is ancient lore which interprets them symbolically, revealing the future for the dreamer or for those whom he or she knows. Aside from the actual content of your dreams, always look for the colour significance as well as its obvious symbolic significance.

COLOUR INDICATORS FOR DREAMS

◆ Dreaming in colour indicates what's coming in the future.
◆ Black-and-white dreams represent the past, showing that it's time to move on.
◆ A nightmare illuminates a backslide, giving a sharp

reminder that the structure of the dreamer's life has been sorely disrupted, and is still festering – a kind of septi-caemia of the memory, which will need constant support during personal growth work while clearance takes place.

◆ Weak colours in a dream suggest that something needs to be looked at immediately.

COLOUR SYMBOLS

There are many books of dream symbols in which to find interpretations of your dreams, none of which explores §and utilises the colour dimension. As dreams and colour are both related to psychology, the colours that appear in your dreams can be interpreted through the colour psychology (see Chapter 7). For instance, doors that will not open suggest difficulties. Take note of the colour of the door or its surround-ing colours. Then refer to Chapter 7 to find clues as to what needs to be addressed in order to free up your life.

A frequent dream symbol is water which, surprisingly, can appear in virtually any colour. Remember whether the water was still, calm or rough. And, what colour it was. Turquoise and choppy water means affairs of the heart are in for a period of turbulence, whereas a gentle, flowing movement indicates your personal relationship is moving along nicely. Calm, smooth water reveals a person feeling caged in their surroundings and unable to free themselves; rough grey water indicates you are trying to break chains that bind you and hold you back.

COLOUR DREAMING

The colour door to your own dreams can be opened by this simple process:

◆ To prepare, take a warm bath and wear white attire.

◆ Use white bed linen.
◆ Relax on the bed.
◆ Take easy breaths and visualise a huge diamond and its many-coloured facets hovering above you.
◆ Allow yourself to stroll gently through its maze of clear, shimmering colours until you calmly slide off into protected, secure, exquisite slumberland, while absorbing the mystic light of creation. The diamond brilliance will immerse you in the mystic light of cosmic creation as you go walkabout amongst the starlight.

Conclusion

Looking closely at colour is a non-invasive way of discovering yourself. Its power is both transcendental and intuitive. Get to know what colour can do for you. Do not delay or neglect responding to this inner knowledge – colour can change your life. Use your mind and body as a prism to find your true colours. It will have an effect on future vibrations when used correctly; it can reverse the tide.

Working with colour, and understanding the connections between yourself and colour, offers a key to good health and vitality. Colour leads into all realms of life on Earth and in the Universe. There is a mystery about colour that bewitches us. It is there for us to use, and there is no better way to use it than by harnessing its strength and benefits for health and healing. Colour enriches our lives.

We are united by colour. For those who seek, colour becomes a glorious influence, fulfilling promises of the future. Get to know what colour can do for you – it can change your life.

index

Lilian Verner-Bonds can be contacted at:

Lilian Verner-Bonds
The Colour-Bonds Association
77 Holders Hill Drive
Hendon
London NW4 1NN
United Kingdom
Phone/fax: 020 8349 3299
Mobile: 07940 349759

For courses, private readings and training, postal
readings, books, tapes and CDs, please send a stamped,
self-addressed envelope for free information.